Martha

from Pooh,

August 16, 1970

Wings in the Meadow

Wings in the Meadow

BY JO BREWER

ILLUSTRATED BY HENRY B. KANE
with diagrams by Jean Husher

HOUGHTON MIFFLIN COMPANY BOSTON
1967

To the four Georges
who have helped in such different ways
to make this book a reality

Acknowledgments

I SHOULD LIKE to express my gratitude to the following sources for co-operation which has made the writing of this book not only possible, but a pleasure:

To the reference department of the Newton Free Library for helping to locate a great deal of obscure information.

To Newton Junior College for allowing me unlimited use of laboratory facilities, and especially to Mr. George W. Hahn, Head of Biological Sciences.

To Harvard University for allowing me access to the Andrew J. Weeks Collection of Lepidoptera and the Museum of Comparative Zoology Library.

To the University of California at Berkeley, Division of Invertebrate Pathology, for assistance in identifying causes of disease in *Danaus plexippus*.

And to these individuals: Dr. Howard E. Evans, Cambridge, Massachusetts; Dr. William T. M. Forbes, Cambridge, Massachusetts; Miss Ruth Haigh, Niagara Falls, Ontario; Miss Ivy Lemon, Massachusetts Audubon Society, Topsfield, Massachusetts; Mr. John Morris, Eastern Point, Gloucester, Massachusetts; Dr. Fred Urquhart, University of Toronto, Ontario.

J. B.

Preface

TO A SCIENTIST, butterflies are not necessarily more interesting than any other form of life. Their beauty is unique; but the beauty of any living thing is only as profound as the interest of the observer. A butterfly on a pin, which may represent an exquisite perfection of pattern, color and design, affords only limited scientific insights. The living adult butterfly on the wing, however, or the serpentine caterpillar crawling on its food plant, represent the mysteries of life itself. These mysteries are still far from understood. Well over half of the butterflies of the world are known only from adult specimens; the egg, larval and pupal stages of their existence having not yet been recognized. Indeed there is not a single species about which we can say that we have complete knowledge. Information is still lacking on the part played by even the most familiar butterflies in any biological community, or its ecosystem.

Wings in the Meadow follows with rare skill the bewildering and little understood path of nature as represented by a single butterfly from egg to death. This absorbing tale is laid not in some exotic far-off land but right at home, in any of a dozen meadows at the end of the road.

We share the obvious delight of the author in discovering the wonders of a world that was not created just for man

alone, but for a vast variety of creatures endowed like us
with the transitory yet dynamic gift of life. The presenta-
tion, pleasingly unpretentious, is not that of a scientific
monograph. It is a narrative which portrays the life of an
individual with fidelity as to detail and validity of interpre-
tation. It is scientifically authentic. Truth is served, but the
bare facts are enhanced by descriptive passages of great
charm, through which the life of a familiar garden butterfly provides us with an enriching and moving experience.

The ways of the investigator are many and devious. One
may find inspiration in an odor-filled laboratory, another in
the sanctuary of a noiseless study. To a third, the moment
of discovery may come in the apparently insignificant and
little understood patch of weeds in his own backyard. If
the latter approach to science commands less attention today than it did a generation ago, it is due in part to a change
in research attitudes caused by the great upsurge and attrac-
tion to modern scientific gadgetry. There is more glamor
in a digital computer than a butterfly net. In no small
measure, however, the change is also brought about by the
increasing rarity of an undisturbed bit of nature.

We are slowly becoming conscious of how man's progress is disturbing nature — how indiscriminate and intensi-
fied misuse, how a detrimental blanket of smog, or a load of
trash, or even one burning match — may tilt the natural
balance of a meadow enough to deliver it a death blow. But
unfortunately we are still putting our meadow communities
to the test of survival under our own terms, without taking
into account the interactions of animal and plant popula-

tions and individuals within them which may bear directly or indirectly on us. When we really know life, when we understand our own environment and the dynamics of the biological forces within it, we will surely have a clearer understanding of ourselves.

It may be man's prejudice that attributes emotion only to creatures with hair and fur, excluding those with feathers and scales. I am sentimental enough to permit the butterfly, Danaus, and his creator the benefit of the doubt. Whenever I enjoy a warm sunny day, I do so with the very ecumenical hope that the other creatures which I see around me are capable of the same sense of enjoyment. Jo Brewer has captured this spirit of oneness with nature in a fine piece of writing which cannot fail to evoke a response from anyone who has known and loved the out-of-doors. *Wings in the Meadow* is a welcome respite from the rigorous discipline of the laboratory, taking us into a world of unspoiled greenness, summer happiness and memories that are still realities in the meadow at the end of the road.

JOHN C. DOWNEY

Contents

Preface by John C. Downey   ix

Introduction   xv

I   A Traveler to the Meadow (*May 21*)   1

II   The Arrival of Danaus (*May 22–28*)   13

III   The Struggle (*May 28–June 4*)   25

IV   The End and the Beginning (*June 4–11*)   37

V   Inside the Locked Room (*June 11–18*)   49

VI   Renaissance (*June 18–19*)   61

VII   Staking Out a Claim (*June 19–21*)   73

VIII   The Pinnacle (*June 19–28*)   83

IX   The Northern Voyage of Danaus (*June 28–July 15*)   97

X   Midway (*July 15–22*)   109

XI   Interlude (*July 15–August 21*)   123

XII   Journey's End (*August 21–September 10*)   135

XIII   The Tidal Wave (*September 17–October 19*)   151

XIV   Another End — Another Beginning (*October 19–November 23*)   161

List of Works Consulted   179

A Short Glossary of Some Biological Terms   183

Maps   188–189

Introduction

What's in a name? That which we call a rose
By any other name would smell as sweet.

SHAKESPEARE

IN 1735 Karl von Linne (Linnaeus), the renowned Swedish naturalist, published the first edition of his *Systema Naturae*, in which he began to establish a system for the classification of plants and animals. It consisted of fourteen pages. He revised and enlarged this work from time to time until 1770, when the fifteenth edition, contained in three volumes, was completed.

His system was based upon a binomial nomenclature in which both a generic and a trivial (or specific) name were given to each species. When he came to the butterflies, the trivial, and in some cases, the generic names which he gave them were those of Greek and Trojan heroes. The binomial system is still in use today, although in the two hundred years and more which have elapsed since 1758, other students of nature have shifted the names about and added new ones in an effort to keep pace with new discoveries. The Monarch butterfly has been variously called *Danaus plexippus, Danais archippus, Danais erippus,* and *Anosia plexippus,* but at the moment he has been given back the trivial name which Linnaeus originally assigned to him, and is again Danaus plexippus.

The "heroes" for whom he was named are rather obscure, and by present-day standards not overly heroic. *Danaus*, the generic name, is that of a son of King Belus. Danaus had fifty daughters, while his twin brother, Aegyptus, had fifty sons. His greatest claim to fame seems to be that he ordered his fifty daughters to marry their fifty cousins and to murder them on their wedding night with long pins, in order to assure his own security, which he feared would eventually be jeopardized by the fifty brothers.

Plexippus, the trivial name, has an even more obscure origin. Little is generally known about Plexippus except that he became involved in an ill-fated boar hunt. He has been described by Swinburne as:

> ... *the violent souled*
> *Plexippus, overswift with hand and tongue.*
> *For hands are fruitful, but the ignorant mouth*
> *Blows and corrupts their work with barren breath.*

During the course of the hunt the boar, after much carnage, was finally wounded by Atalanta, the huntress, and later killed by Meleager, a nephew of Plexippus. Meleager, who had become enamored of Atalanta, gave the hide and the head of the animal to her, saying that as she had been the first to draw blood from it, she should have the spoils. This so enraged Plexippus, who wanted the hide for himself, that he fought with his nephew who soon slew him.

It is ironical that Linnaeus should have chosen the names of two such miserable heroes for this remarkable insect who, in the order of Lepidoptera, holds a fairly major position on the evolutionary scale, while the far more distinguished name *Parnassius apollo* was conferred upon a butterfly that in a number of ways is far more primitive. Perhaps, as has been suggested, this was done in a moment of whimsy.

It is also ironical that in the *Handbook of Biological Data* (1956) the Monarch is listed as a pest. It is even more difficult to determine the reason for this, since the larva of the Monarch eats nothing but milkweed, which in the same volume is also listed as a pest. If milkweed is a pest, then surely something which destroys it ought to be an asset. But milkweed seems hardly more of a pest than the Monarch. It sometimes springs up in fields and pastures, but grazing animals do not bother to eat it, and it is rarely found to any extent in well-cultivated areas. Anyone who has tried to grow milkweed will testify to the small amount which sprouts compared to the number of seeds planted. It has no commercial value (although the early settlers used its floss to stuff quilts), but it does have lovely fragrant blossoms, and its silken parachutes are among the most interesting phenomena of the fall. I leave it to the reader to decide whether or not these two interdependent forms of life — the milkweed which supports the larvae of the Monarch, and the Monarch butterfly which pollenizes the milkweed — should be classed with ragweed, locusts, Japanese beetles, witch grass and gypsy moths, as pests.

Jo Brewer

I

A Traveler to the Meadow
(May 21)

Nothing is wasted — nothing lost.
The bird that thrusts against the air
Does so only at the cost
Of other wings no longer there.

JOHN RITCHEY

MR. STEVENS ALLOWED his front acres to remain a
Meadow. Once a year, at the end of July, he mowed a
three-foot strip on each side of the path, but the rest of
the time everything grew there that wanted to, and as
far as Mr. Stevens was concerned everything that grew
there was a wild flower, and there was no such thing as
a weed.

The front acres were separated from the street by a low,
crumbling stone wall which, being overgrown with poison
ivy, was an ideal hiding place for the chipmunks who
could be seen scampering along it or peering from its
crevices at almost any hour of the day. An opening in the
wall was the beginning of a path leading through Mr.
Stevens' front acres to a wood lot, in the midst of which
was his own private citadel. On days when he found himself too far removed from the real world, he would take
his jeep, drive through the opening in the wall, through his
Meadow, and into the woods to his cabin.

It made him happy to be the owner of a Meadow. Hardly anyone owned a meadow any more. All of the land around his had been made into small choice estates, groomed and lovely, and carefully planned as to the size and color of each flower and shrub to give the most aesthetic pleasure to the largest number of people, while Mr. Stevens' Meadow gave no immediate pleasure to any-one but himself. Since he never used it for a pasture, he didn't mind that tansy and yarrow and milkweed — daisies and Bouncing Bet — shared it with grass and clover. Since he never used it for a market garden, he didn't mind the woodchucks who dug great caverns as big as his foot and as deep as his knee under the roots of the waist-high vege-tation. If a small brown rabbit crossed the path of his jeep, as was often the case, he only chuckled, because no matter how much greenery the rabbit and his presumably large family might consume, the Meadow would be none the worse for it. He didn't even mind the persistent croak-ing of the redwings, a sound like rather musical rusty hinges blowing in the wind from dawn to dusk; because from his citadel in the woods their creakings became just another faraway sound — faint and rather friendly — like people at a church picnic.

And so from year to year, the Meadow lay serene and undisturbed and alive. In October, the trees at the edges of the Meadow dropped their leaves in a gold and scarlet rain, and the seeds of the milkweed rose like floating stars to meet them. By November, all the stalks and blades, victims of the winds, the rains, and senescence, lay prone, waiting for the snow. Mr. Stevens barred the doors and windows of his cabin and felled a log across the path, even though he knew that soon the snow would be too deep for any car to pass. Then winter came, spreading its pallid cloths, and the Meadow slept and the chipmunks lay curled in furry balls in the ground — and the larvae of the red milkweed beetle lay curled in fat lozenges in the roots of the milkweed. A mourning cloak butterfly which had emerged from the drab prison of his chrysalis just before the first frost had wilted the goldenrod now took shelter in a hollow log lying at the end of the Meadow. His tightly closed wings, invisible against the rotting wood, gave no hint of the burnished brass and mahogany shield they enclosed. This he would present to the world only when the first warm sun of February penetrated the dark of his hibernaculum.

March touched the rich soil beneath last year's tangle of dead flowers, melting its frozen crust with beneficent fingertips, and April summoned across this slippery quagmire an infinitesimal greenness — a fuzz of green pubescent hair . . . and so came spring. Minute green caterpillars which had lain in a frozen sleep all during the long New England winter began to creep blindly and sluggishly through the wet tangle, until with miraculous accuracy they came to rest upon the first tender shoots of meadow clover. By May, the red clover was in bloom, the grasses and the milkweed above knee high, and each meristem was vying with its myriad neighbors for a place in the sun. Lying concealed beneath the sodden carpet of last year's

stalks and among the grassy spires, the awakening population of a miniature metropolis was busily creating the intri-
cate balance, enacting the ancient ritual by which some
would live and some would die — by which nothing would
be lost — by which the dead would nourish the living and
the living reproduce in kind in an incorruptible circle as
long as the Meadow remained . . .

On the twenty-first of May the weather was blue and
gold and more still than the tiny rustling of a green grass
snake as he glided away from his sunning spot on the path
into an invisible tunnel which opened for a brief moment
and then closed again behind him. At twelve noon, Danaus,
the mother, flying north just barely above the tops of the

trees came to the Meadow, flew across it, wheeled and turned. Somehow she knew that she had found the place where she would lay the last of her eggs. She was desperately tired, and her wings — once sparkling with color — had grown dull and ragged. Her feet were becoming brittle, and her body, once full and rounded with eggs, was shriveled and long and thin. The sense of urgency which had carried her northward for so many days was exhausted, and she sought only a place where she could finish her work and sleep.

She glided down over the Meadow and began a long zig-zag flight which took her back and forth across it, close to the tops of the weeds and grasses, stopping occasionally to rest or suck the nectar of a clover blossom through the long coiling tube that was her mouth. The 12,000 facets of her marvelous insect eyes told her where the sun lay and warned her of the approach of any other creature, for although they could probably not help her to pinpoint the location of any single object, they could detect light and motion far more expertly than the eyes of almost any other living creature. It was by some mysterious combination of senses having their origin in her antennae, her feet, and the spiracles along the sides of her body through which she breathed that she knew there were fresh young milkweed plants in the field upon which her progeny might feed.

She did not know how many miles she had flown, nor how many eggs she had laid. She had passed the winter months in the northern part of the state of Georgia close to a small country town. Many of the other Monarch butterflies in the huge congregation with which she had traveled south the previous autumn had continued on to Florida or along the Gulf coast to Mexico or into Texas, but she and some others had ended their journey sooner than the rest and found for themselves a tall live oak tree at the edge of the town where, since there were so few of them, they had roosted undetected during all the cold hours and the dark hours of the winter, sallying forth only occasionally to feed or warm their wings in the sun.

With the coming of March, some indescribable nostalgia had awakened in her, and she had left the live oak tree never to return. She had started to fly north — very slowly at first, because she would only fly in the bright sunlight, and in March many days were filled with rain and many other days and nights were very cold. Her instinct told her to take shelter when the rain came. Her wings and even her body were waterproofed to a certain extent, so that she could, if need be, alight on the water and rise again. But this was an emergency protection which would soon wear away, and after even twenty minutes of exposure to heavy rain, she would become waterlogged and unable to fly. Much of her protection from the water was provided by her hard exoskeleton, but protection from the cold was another matter. Unlike a warm-blooded animal, she was not equipped with a thermostatic control. There was no device within her to regulate her own bodily warmth and thus help her to withstand freezing temperatures. The temperature of her body rose and fell with the weather as though she were part of it. On the hottest days, she flew the fastest and the farthest, but with the coolness of night her body gradually grew numb, and if the temperature dropped to forty-five degrees, she was no longer able to move. Therefore, when the sun began to redden, she sought a friendly tree, and always clung to a leaf on the southeast side of it, so that when morning came and the first warm rays of the sun penetrated the blackness of her body, she could continue on her way.

On the fortieth day of her journey, another Monarch intercepted her flight, and after one brief ecstatic flight into the sun, they mated. . . . When the sun rose the following morning, it found her resting on a small branch, her mate by her side. But now, for the first time, she was filled with a compelling urgency, and in an hour she had flown her separate way, her brief courtship forgotten. For almost two weeks she flew, and by the time she reached the Meadow, she had deposited more than 400 eggs on the soft tips of the milkweed plants along her route.

At noon when she arrived at the Meadow, she had already been flying for two hours. Once, in crossing the street, she had almost been crushed against a speeding automobile, but the violent contortions of the air as the automobile whirled past had hurled her high above the windshield in a giddy arc, catching her in a vortex of dust and fumes from which she escaped only by wheeling and plunging into the dirt by the roadside. Another time, a kingbird had started in pursuit of her, but her flight had been too quick and too erratic and he had soon abandoned the chase.

Danaus, the mother, chose the food for her young with infinite care. She descended slowly onto a milkweed leaf close to the apical meristem of the plant she had chosen. She walked along it, and, apparently satisfied that no other creature had been there before her, she grasped the edges of the leaf with her sharp tarsi. Then holding her wings high she bent her abdomen in a perfect semicircle and deposited a single jewellike egg on the soft fuzz of the leaf's underside. After laying each egg, she rested for a long time, for she was very tired. On the third plant, an infinitesimal motion and an unfamiliar odor warned her that a spider lay hidden under the adjoining leaf, and she flew away in a panic. She rose so abruptly that one of her brittle feet, caught in a single strand of the spider's web, broke off and was left hanging from the leaf where she had been standing a moment before. She rejected one plant on which she detected the eggs of egele, the harlequin caterpillar, and alighted instead on the uninhabited stalk beside it. On still another stalk had been deposited a colony of the bright yellow eggs of acraea, the salt-marsh moth, which would hatch and separate and become fearsome hairy caterpillars twice as quick to move and nearly twice as large as her own offspring, capable of defoliating all the milkweed for a yard around. Perhaps her instinct told her how badly her one small offspring would fare against such competition, for she flew far away from this spot and did not return to it. These two plants she rejected, but she did not see the earwig lying flat and motionless between the small parallel tip leaves of the next plant she chose, and she left an egg scarcely two inches from where he was hidden.

That day Danaus the mother laid eleven eggs, and then it was three o'clock in the afternoon. She was weary unto death. She flew to the back edge of the Meadow looking for a low branch under which she might sleep, but her motions had become clumsy and labored, and in reaching for the branch she lost a second foot. Now she had only two tarsi with which to support herself, for her two foremost feet, like those of all her tribe, had, over eons of evolutionary time, lost their usefulness, and were held crossed against her thorax. She clawed at the branch for a moment and fluttered to the ground. Her wings became entangled in a mesh of wild raspberry, and fluttering desperately to free herself, she broke the strong costal vein of her left forewing, which had sustained her flight south in the autumn and northward again in the spring, a distance of over six hundred miles. Now she would fly no more. She crept down into the thick grasses and vines, deeper and deeper until she lay wedged securely among them, close to their roots.

The golden sun could no longer cast its warmth over the surface of her wings. Her long proboscis would never again find nectar in a blossom. She lay still and waited. Over her head a catbird flew into a tree bordering the field and perched there, flipping his tail and making saucy sport of his neighbors. A honeybee buzzed as he visited the blossoms of the raspberry. An hour passed . . . two hours. In some distant part of the Meadow a pheasant uttered his hollow astonished "CRAWK!" and exploded suddenly into the air, routed, perhaps by some small scurrying animal. The sun sent pale shafts through the trees, spreading over the Meadow a gray and silver patchwork. Back in the woods there was a thrush's watery voice and then only the littlest noises — high and multitudinous and indefinable — pricked the dusk.

Still she waited. Three hours . . . four hours . . . somewhere in the distance a whippoorwill began his clean repetitious monologue. Suddenly a great beam of light pierced the darkness where she lay, as Mr. Stevens came in his jeep through the opening in the wall, through the Meadow and into the woods to his citadel.

This was the last thing she saw. In the morning, the foraging black ants found her and carried her away.

II

The Arrival of Danaus
(May 22–28)

Quant'e bella giovinezza
Che ci sfugge tutta via;
Chi vuol' esser' lieto sia.
Di doman' non c'e certezza.

How beautiful is youth
Which so quickly flies;
Let who will be merry.
For of tomorrow there is no certainty.

LORENZO DE' MEDICI

ON THE MORNING of May 22, when Mr. Stevens came out of his woods to survey his Meadow, he saw many things. First of all, there was a phoebe's nest under construction beneath the eaves of his cabin, and he sat out in a camp chair watching bits of moss and grass being woven into it while he drank his coffee. Then he discovered by his well a large hole under a fallen log, which he presumed to have been made by an animal, but a preliminary search failed to disclose what sort of animal. A pair of redstarts were darting about in the trees bordering the Meadow, and as he watched them flashing their red and yellow epaulets, he was aware that from higher in the trees — high in all the trees — there came a piping sound — thin, high and clear and beautiful — the sound of little songs from little throats.

The oak leaves were yellow-green and the size of his

thumb, and long yellow catkins dropping from the end of each twig shivered and danced, set in motion by an invisible source. The warblers — the Tennessee and the Canada warbler, the Blackburnian and the parula, the yellow warbler and the chestnut-sided warbler — flashed like jewels in a green crown, but their world was too far away for Mr. Stevens to see. He stood peering into the branches without success for several minutes before he continued his walk along the path into his Meadow, leaving the exploration of the tree-top jungle for another time. He heard a meadow lark pouring forth its lovely flutelike melody at the far end of the field, but the song ceased and the timid bird disappeared in the grasses before he was close enough to see it.

He stopped to watch the redwings, who were too busily engaged to take notice of him. Close to his hand — almost touching it — was a stem of milkweed, and suspended from the underside of one of its smallest leaves was a creamy white droplet. It could have been a drop of milky juice left there when some small sap-sucking insect had withdrawn his sharp beak from the leaf's vein. Mr. Stevens, intently watching the redwings, did not see it. If he had seen it, he would not have known what it was. His interest in winged creatures was confined to the birds of his Meadow, many of which he could name by their songs long before finding the feathered throat in which the song originated. In his mind insects were purely incidental to flowers, and of value only to the birds who ate them. If he had been asked where butterflies came from, he might have answered that butterflies laid eggs which hatched out baby butterflies, and if he had thought about a butterfly egg at all, he would doubtless have dismissed it as something too insignificant to be interesting. He continued his study of the redwings, whose young he would someday see trying out their stubby wings and tumbling ineptly back into the tall grass.

But life does not begin with the building of a nest, or the laying of an egg, or the first flight of a bird. It does not begin anywhere. It simply *is*, and continues to be. It exists irrevocably, regardless of the ravages made upon it by other manifestations of itself.

The minute egg of Danaus the mother was not created to be seen by the eyes of a man. Had it been a thousand times greater than it was, it could have been an Easter egg wrought of ivory by the Czar's master craftsman, engraved with incredible precision and taste — a priceless treasure for a royal child. But what eye can see the egg of a butterfly? — except perhaps an eye much smaller than the egg itself, or eyes which take the trouble to examine it through a more powerful manmade eye.

But more marvelous even than the sculptured chorion was the fragile world within it, for it held not only life but the possibility of transformation from life to life — from one living creature to another seemingly unrelated living form. And the source of the power which orders this transformation, whether infinitely large or infinitely small, remains a mystery.

The finest strand of silk is not finer than the tip of the

ovariole where the egg has its origin, and yet in these microscopic tubes in the abdomen of the mother, each germ cell
divides again and again, each new cell moving along its
widening tube toward a common oviduct and growing as
it moves, until its nucleus is surrounded by yolk materials,
by a vitelline membrane, and finally by the lovely chorion
which envelops it completely but for a minute aperture
through which the sperm will enter.

After Danaus the mother had mated, the sperm secreted
into a pouch in her body followed a tortuous passage ending
at a point opening into a common oviduct — a point which
all her eggs must traverse a moment before being laid. So
precise were the biological timing mechanisms involved,
that Danaus the mother, having completed mating at sundown, laid her first fertile eggs before ten o'clock of the
following morning.

Mr. Stevens made careful note of the area of the field
into which the redwings had repeatedly descended. Later,
perhaps, he would try to find the nest — to see the speckled
eggs. He drew a bead on the spot between a dead branch
behind it and the stalk of milkweed almost under his hand,
and to mark his starting point, he snipped off the top of the
milkweed with his thumbnail and dropped it on the path.
White milk flowed from the open wound — a perfect
marker.

Of the eleven eggs laid by Danaus the mother in Mr.
Stevens' Meadow, one was eaten by the earwig which crept
from its hiding-place and devoured it moments after it had

been laid. One perished on the withered milkweed which Mr. Stevens had dropped on the path, and one which was not fertile remained intact on its leaf.

In three days, the remaining eight eggs developed shining black tops — the heads of embrionic caterpillars. These soon chewed their way to freedom, ate their shells, and then lay exhausted, each under the leaf of his own plant. When the first tiny larva crawled forth on the morning of May twenty-fifth, his appearance was completely inconsequential, both as to color and size. He was an infinitesimal speck in a wide expanse of greenness which harbored hundreds of other newborn creatures as small and as sallow as he. His black beadlike head trailed a putty-colored body from which protruded minute hairs. His overall length was only two millimeters. He could hardly have been distinguished from the larva cradled in a clover leaf which would some-day become a yellow or an orange Colias butterfly, or from those curled under leaves of elm and hops which would later be angle wings. But since he lay newly hatched on a milkweed leaf, he could be neither of these.

So it was that on his first day of life, it was only the plant upon which he lay that gave identity to Danaus the son — Danaus of the Golden Wings, for this was he. And being hungry, but still too small to penetrate the surface of the leaf with his tiny horizontally opposed jaws, he nibbled tentatively at the fuzzy pubescence on its under side. By this act only was he known to be of the tribe of the Danaids, for among all butterflies only the young Danaidae feed upon the leaves of milkweed.

But his inconspicuous appearance in no way detracted from the tremendous achievement which had culminated in his having arrived in the world an independent self-sufficient perfect individual. This remarkable act of re-creation had been accomplished in three and a half days from the time that one sperm had entered one egg consisting of a single nucleus surrounded by simple cytoplasm. Until this moment of fertilization, the entire egg had been growing and then dividing, producing with each division a new egg cell which had likewise grown and divided, but which, of itself, had held no potential for further development. But upon the union of egg cell and sperm cell, division had begun to take place only in the newly fused nucleus which now contained in its chromosomes all the hereditary traits inherent in both the egg and the sperm nuclei. The new cells, as they formed, had drifted toward the outside of the egg until there was a layer of cells completely enclosing the protoplasmic yolk material. At this point, an invisible substance, originating perhaps in some embryonic gland, stimulated perhaps by light, perhaps by heat, perhaps by an unknown and equally invisible hormonal substance, was spread over the cells, and in that moment it was determined how the larva should be formed. It was only after this mysterious occurrence that the cells on one side of the egg which would form the legs of the caterpillar, all his mouth parts and his eyes, had begun to thicken and multiply. Other cells began to form his muscle, his digestive system, his heart, and still others his glands and skin. A few hours after the first wave, another substance as mysterious as the first had been spread over the embryo, and certain cells, thereafter, had grown dormant and would not awaken again until it was time for the chrysalis or even the butterfly to be formed. The sleeping cells which would one day be his wings migrated to the thoracic region, and those which would be his reproductive organs to the abdomen. His nervous system was formed, and the spiracles and tracheoles through which he would breathe. The spinning gland upon which his life would often depend and his spinneret were shaped and perfected, and by the time he left his shell, there were in this miniscule creature, all the ingredients necessary for his complete metamorphosis, and all were equipped to develop, to delay development, or to cease development at exactly the right moment in his complete life cycle. By three o'clock of that same day, there were eight larvae in various parts of Mr. Stevens' Meadow. Each ate his egg shell, rested, nibbled, rested, nibbled. By the time six hours had passed, they were able to bite through the leaf and they left little tell-tale holes edged with milk-weed juice to mark the end of each small banquet.

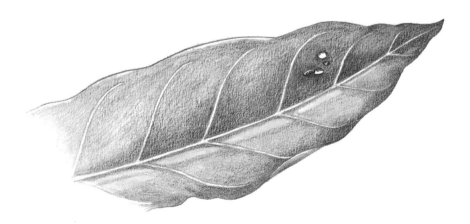

The weather had been very hot for three days and three nights. But just before dawn on the morning of the twenty-seventh of May, a sudden shower soaked the meadow and freshened the air. During these three days, Danaus the son had doubled in size. In his first twenty-four hours, he had chewed four small holes in his leaf and consumed an amount of milkweed equal to his own weight. Parts of his skin had darkened until his body was encircled by nine chocolate-colored bands. Now his skin was stretched so tightly about him that he could eat no more and his black face mask, which had once covered his whole head, had become a tight black glass button pinching his mouth. The time had come for him to shed his first skin. With his two anal prolegs, he grasped a bit of the silk which he had spun, and summoning all his little strength, pushed his head forward until, splitting his skin at the thorax, he was able to wriggle his way out of it. This herculean task, which taxed his every muscle, required nearly three hours of his life.

Unlike the little green grass snake sliding silently through the grass below him, he had, in shedding his skin, also shed his skeleton. There were no bones in his body to help in supporting his vital organs. His tough elastic exoskeleton alone performed this indispensable function, and, therefore, whenever he outgrew it and cast it aside, he would lie, as now, vulnerable and helpless until enough time had elapsed for the new skin beneath the old one to harden. Five times he would have to cross this perilous frontier as he proceeded from one instar to the next, and the fifth time he would vanish forever.

In another part of the Meadow, the smallest of all the Monarch larvae had crawled through the hole he had eaten to the top side of his leaf and the pink rays of the sun coming through the trees fell upon him and warmed his little body. Elsewhere in the field, the yellow eggs of acraea, the salt-marsh moth, had all hatched at once, and the black hair-thin larvae had quickly dissipated to other parts of the leaf — to other parts of the plant, unnoticed.

By mid-afternoon, the unseasonable heat had returned, and now, at sundown, the mists began to gather in the bottomlands. By morning most of the Meadow was wrapped in long scarves of fog. Danaus the son, lying on the springy pubescence beneath his leaf, was safe, but the smallest larva, who had crawled to the top of his leaf, lay drowned in the little beads of moisture which had settled over and around him before he sought to find shelter.

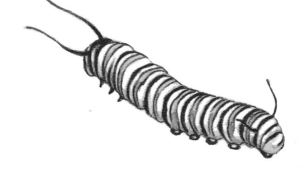

III

The Struggle
(May 28–June 4)

Are God and Nature then at strife,
   That Nature lends such evil dreams?
   So careful of the type she seems,
So careless of the single life . . .

TENNYSON

*Emergence of polyxenes,
the black swallowtail*

HAVING MOLTED, Danaus the son, now in his second instar, had begun to show the characteristics which could identify him for the rest of his larval life. His chalk white body was ringed with black and pale yellow, and tiny horn-like protuberances had appeared behind his head. Now he had but one obligation to his present self, his future self, and to his race, and that was to eat. In the next two weeks he would have to eat not only enough to cause himself to live and grow to maturity, but enough to nourish the chrysalis into which he would then be transformed. He ate randomly at first, and soon his leaf was perforated with holes of various sizes through which he could crawl at will. He ate and rested alternately, day and night for three more days before molting again. By this time the redwings had finished their nest and the drab little female sat patiently upon her three spotted eggs while her mate flew from perch to perch flashing his military attire and loudly voicing his uncomplimentary opinion of every creature which ventured within fifty feet of his nest. Frequently, he descended into the Meadow in search of food. Not being epicurean in his tastes, he combed the grasses and the treetops for whatever bits of nourishment might be there — beetles, spiders, even a few of last year's dried-up seeds.

The red milkweed beetle had crawled from his pupa case in the roots of the milkweed plant. Looked upon as marvels of creation, these beetles were indeed superb. Their bright rose-colored elytra, stylishly decorated with jet black disks, lay folded across their backs, while their long graceful antennae fanned sinuously back and forth. But the repulsive nature of their habits more than counteracted their beauty. Several pairs could be found on one plant at almost any hour of the day, and their copious excrement fouled all its leaves, leaving upon their chewed surfaces not only splotches of dung, but an oily poisonous-looking coating which rendered them repellent to any other form of life. In addition to this, the creatures were usually found copulating and feeding at the same time, and the total picture which they presented was one of unbridled debauchery and slovenliness.

However, the redwing had no qualms about adding them to his diet. He swooped down without warning, and snatched up a pair in his sharp beak without even bothering to alight.

Danaus the son was nearly blind, being able to see only light and the direction from which it came through the six pinpoint-sized lenses, which were his eyes. However, the survival of a species does not depend upon its sight alone, but upon its ability to adapt and to compensate; to adapt to the circumstances into which it had been channeled by the whims of evolution, and to compensate for the lack of one sense by the cultivation of another. Danaus had learned to feel. He could feel the texture of his leaf or a change in the wind. If his plant were touched, he could feel its slightest tremor, or if a nearby animal started suddenly, he could feel the vibrations in the air caused by its quick flight or startled cry.

But most important of all, he could feel the silken filament of his own spinning, which was always beneath his feet. It was a guide line during his explorations — a ball of twine given to him by some distant Ariadne. It was the line to which he must moor his old skin whenever he molted, and it would be the anchor for his cremaster when the time came for his chrysalis to form. This tiny strand, which originated in a gland in his abdomen and was secreted through a hair-fine tube beneath his lower lip, was indeed his lifeline, for without it he would surely have perished.

He traveled along it, seeking out the boundaries of his empire. There were other inhabitants of his leaf. There was a microscopic inchworm, and there was a pale yellow aphid, a scarlet spider and a transparent mite, each only half the size of his head. To them his network of silk strands was a never-ending obstacle to progress, and he in all his magnificent five millimeters was a formidable mon-

ster capable of crushing any one of them to death under one prickly proleg. Of all this he was entirely unaware, and he continued to eat the ground out from under their feet, having no interest whatever in the preservation of other forms of life.

By the first week of June, the spring population of the Meadow was approaching its peak, what with the blackbirds' eggs, the confetti of yellow, orange and white sulphur butterflies falling on the powder of daisies, and the various small catacombs leading to nests full of sightless, hairless abortions belonging either to chipmunks or field mice, or perhaps rabbits. The black swallowtail, polyxenes, as a horny brown chrysalid, had survived the predations of winter birds and animals by resembling the stub of a broken twig on a small branch. Her tribe had begun now to emerge. The first two lovely black and yellow butterflies had mated, and the female was busily laying her eggs on the tender tips of Queen Anne's lace, while the male, with unconcerned élan, feasted upon the nectar of clover and honeysuckle.

A worn and threadbare squirrel left her hole in an oak tree to search for nourishment in the nearby nest of a bluejay, but the objections were so vehement and so painful that some other food supply had to be found, and this time it was a mushroom growing under Mr. Stevens' front porch. The bluejay, meanwhile, according to his own inequitable standards, made his meal from the egg of a robin.

It is the instinct of an animal to protect his young and

provide them with food, just as it is his function to maintain his species by procreation. But it is also his function to become the food of other species which, being nourished by him, are also able to survive. And so it was that the young bluejay would one day test his wings, leave his nest, and alight on Mr. Stevens' path, where the kestrel, perched on a branch above his head, would swoop down upon him and carry him off in his talons. So it was that the young squirrel, wandering too far from his nest in the exuberance of his first freedom, would fall prey to the red fox whose den was under the fallen log by Mr. Stevens' well. So it was with a young Danaid who, in his third instar, was feeding openly and fearlessly on the top of his milk-weed leaf, when he was captured and devoured by a redstart.

On this same day, a gray tachina fly flew across the Meadow. She could have been mistaken for a common housefly had she been a little smaller, a little darker, and a little less hairy. But unlike the housefly, she was too fastidious to lay her eggs in carrion. Luck was with her for a brief space of time. She came upon the larvae of the mourning cloak, which eight days earlier had hatched from two hundred pale iridescent eggs, and were now feeding in groups of eight or ten on the same branch of a willow tree. She alighted on one of them, and in an instant had found her way between the hairy spines which protruded from its body in all directions, for the grubs of the tachina would be nourished not by leaves or grasses, but by the flesh of other insects. She laid just one egg on the flexible skin beneath the protecting bristles. She was thus busily engaged in flying from one to another parasitizing each in turn when her short span of luck ran out. A barn swallow flashed by, snatched her out of the air and disappeared over the trees. But the tachina had accomplished her mission. The shells of her eggs would soon open, and the tiny grub in each one would reach out and pierce the skin of the caterpillar on which it had been deposited. The grub would then leave his shell and crawl into the incision he had made to begin a life of darkness nourished by an unwilling host.

Another tachina flying close above the meadow grasses found one of the Danaids. She buzzed around and about the plant and, unbeknown to him, laid three of her eggs within his reach — eggs so microscopic in size that he was not even aware of it when he ate them, and so hard-shelled that they rolled unharmed down his esophagus and into his digestive tract. Here they hatched. The Danaid would not die at once, but would live out his caterpillarhood nourishing the grub of the tachina fly, who would feed first upon his bodily fluids and lastly on his vital organs, never taking enough to kill until he himself should be ready to pupate. Then the grub would worm his way out through a hole in the skin of his host and drop to the ground hanging from a long thread of silk. Here among the grasses he would form a brown egg-shaped pupa, while the Danaid would die suspended from his leaf.

The varieties of tachina flies on the wing were legion. They preyed upon the bees and upon the beetles and upon egele, the Harlequin caterpillar.* One sought out turnus, the yellow swallowtail, who had crawled untimely from his birch leaf nest to feed. Another found a colony of tussock caterpillars which, had they lived, would have become gypsy moths — a species so prolific that the second generation of them would have destroyed the foliage surrounding the Meadow. The tachina's gift to the world was the newly hatched maggot which she deposited with precision and efficiency in each of them.

The sulphurs and the white cabbage butterflies had nothing to fear from the tachinas, but their ranks had already been decimated by various tiny ichneumon wasps, hardly larger than gnats. Other ichneumon wasps had ravaged the colony of acraea larvae which were now ten millimeters long and as gray and furry as kittens. Thus, in the Meadow there was a constant interchange of life and death — a fierce and gentle struggle — a mesh woven of predations from which a few of each species would always escape, and to these few would be entrusted the task of preserving their kind.

On the fourth of June Danaus the son entered his fifth instar. He lay under a leaf as he had lain three other times before molting. This time he had spun not just one strand,

---

* Different caterpillars are hosts to different species of tachina flies. Those mentioned in this chapter are as follows:

HOST	PARASITIC TACHINA
gypsy moth	*Compsilura concinnata*
monarch	*Lespesia archippivora*
Harlequin moth	*Lespesia frenchii*
tiger swallowtail	*Lespesia frenchii*
mourning cloak	*Euphorocera claripennis*

but a little sheet of silk into which he had firmly fastened his anal prolegs. He lay overcome with lassitude, while the molting fluid loosed by endocrine glands just inside of his body once again seeped between his old and new skins, dissolving the inner layer of his rubbery exoskeleton and leaving a slippery fluid surrounding the new skin beneath it.

At his first molting, he had struggled wildly to escape from the enmeshing trap of his skin. Now he was older and perhaps wiser, and he used his strength with economy. His muscles flowed in little ripples, and he arched his head forward, twisting it from side to side as he worked to loosen his skin. Satisfied finally that he was free, he lifted the anterior half of his body from the leaf, thrusting it out even beyond its full length, splitting his skin at the thorax. With a gesture of exquisite grace, he bent back in a semicircle as he withdrew his six true legs, and continuing the long smooth undulation, he curved his head forward once more as he freed his eight walking prolegs and with one after the other stepped onto the leaf. Then clinging to the leaf with one pair of prolegs only, he braced himself in a double arch, straining against the vacuum which had been created in his old skin, and pulling his abdomen free, allowed it, too, to settle slowly back onto the leaf. The striped chitinous head capsule from which the larva derives its name* had not yet been shed and indeed was a mask covering his face. He rubbed it against the rib of the leaf until it broke loose and fell to the ground. Now he lay still. His face and all his legs were creamy and transparent. His

* The Latin word *larva* means mask or skeleton.

chalk white body was handsomely striped with glossy black
and bright yellow, and the pairs of filaments projecting
from his thorax and abdomen, which had begun as nearly
invisible stubs, were now ten millimeters long and lay flatly
folded against his back waiting to dry.

In an hour his skin had hardened. His six true legs — the
useless stubs which would soon be the long slender legs of
the butterfly — glistened like patent leather and his filaments waved gently as he moved. Now he began to eat
furiously. He started with his old skin — a good source of
protein — and having finished this, crawled to the end of
the leaf and began to consume it methodically, beginning
with the tip and eating everything including the center rib.
His excretions fell into the grass, eventually returning to
the earth his own weight in soil-enriching materials. When
he had finished one leaf, he proceeded along the plant's stem
to another. He made no effort to conceal himself, but
threw all his energies into his voracious eating.

From his perch on a young tree, the redwing saw him.
He cocked his head for a moment, flew upward briefly,
and dropped onto the adjoining plant for a closer inspection
of this large and unusual morsel. But Danaus had seen the
faint shadow of his wings and had felt the shaking of his
own plant. Before the bird could strike out, he curled himself into a wheel and rolled to the ground where he
lay motionless, camouflaged by the multi-colored meadow
grasses.

When he dared venture to move once more, he found
himself almost hopelessly lost in a morass of unfamiliar

vegetation through which he lurched and blundered trying to find a foothold. He had never left his plant before, and he had no way now of knowing where it stood. Blind as he was, he could not possibly see it, nor could he smell it unless his feet should touch it. He could only tell from which direction the light came, so with the distant sun as his only guide, he managed to right himself and started to climb upward. But he had become solid and heavy, and his weight was cumbersome. Many of the grass blades up which he endeavored to climb would not support him, and time after time, he fell back into the thick forest of stems. He floundered through buttercups and clover, the young shoots of Bouncing Bet, tansy and goldenrod, falling and climbing, writhing and twisting to find the sun, and starting anew, for nearly two hours, when suddenly his feet encountered a pungent and familiar fragrance. Moments later, he was feasting once more, his long journey forgotten, his long filaments waving with casual grace.

IV

The End and the Beginning

(June 4–11)

Sweet are the uses of adversity;
Which, like the toad, ugly and venomous,
Wears yet a precious jewel in his head . . .

SHAKESPEARE

FOR FOUR DAYS and five nights he fed almost continuously, eating his way down the plant leaf by leaf, sometimes starting at the leaf's tip, sometimes biting gouges out of its edge. On the fifth day, he measured more than fifty millimeters in length and was sleek and fat with skin the texture of Dresden china. On this day, some obscure instinct told him that his travail was accomplished. He ceased his eating and began to wander restlessly up and down the plant's stalk, onto the naked leaf ribs, lifting his head occasionally and swaying from side to side as though he were trying to discover in the air some clue to the whereabouts of his future resting place. Finally he chose a large leaf about two feet from the ground, below the tops of the surrounding grasses and weeds, but high enough to escape the notice of field mice. His faultless instinct told him that his chrysalis must be suspended in such a way that the wings of the butterfly, when it emerged, could hang free until they had expanded and dried. If the leaf he chose should fall, he would no longer have strength nor capacity to find his way back. His resting place must be secure for the two weeks necessary to complete his metamorphosis, for once locked in his chrysalis he would be only a disembodied, immobilized, formless spark of life. So, having chosen his leaf, he carefully secured it to the plant's stem with a tight little rope of silk. After he had finished this task, he crawled to the underside of the leaf, and began to spin a compact button, scarcely larger than a seed pearl on the center rib. He could not see what he had made, but he could feel it with the pads which served him as feet. He walked over it very slowly and carefully, testing its position with each step, and when he had reached it with the extreme end of his abdomen, he clamped his black anal prolegs securely into it. Now began the last long hours of waiting — the silent motionless hours preceding the ceremony which would separate him forever from his larval life.

It is in the nature of living creatures to cling to life with the greatest tenacity when the promise life holds is least. When the cup is full, the precious liquid is spilled with reckless joy — when nearly drained, the last few drops become a priceless treasure. So it seemed to be with Danaus in these last minutes. Very gradually — very slowly — as though each decision were made with profound regret, he loosed the grip of his prolegs one at a time, until the last little fleshy pad was his only support. With this he clung to the leaf for a long time. Then in one sudden moment he fell free, and his body was swinging head down from the silk button which he had spun. For the larva it was a ceremony marking the acceptance of death at the end of life, tempered by centuries of intuitive knowledge that life, in turn, would follow this seeming death. For whether he knew it or not, the *larva* was already dying. He had been dying since his wandering had begun. He could no longer eat, and his powers of regeneration and ambulation were gone. Already the process of histolysis by which his organs would be destroyed had begun, and he felt again the familiar lethargy — this time infinitely more profound.

And whether he knew it or not, out of his approaching larval death would come a new life, and it was for this that he himself had lived. For the larva himself had no ability to create — no power to reproduce himself in kind. He was born only to nourish the life which was to come — a life which could only reproduce and lacked the power to grow or to develop.

He hung from his leaf, a fleshy hook, for a day and a night, when like a participant in some pagan ritual, he began to chew away his own mouth — or so it seemed. In reality this painstaking labor was an indispensable part of his metamorphosis, for when he again awakened to life it would be to drink the nectar of flowers, not to devour their leaves. The work of the strong biting mandibles was done. The china-like surface of his skin began to wrinkle and the clear colors to fade. The black filaments hung limp and twisted. Stretching himself taut once more, he pushed his skin in black folds away from his head until at last the split came . . . and the creature which began to issue from this last larval skin, helpless and blind and formless, bore no resemblance whatever to the creature which had spawned it. Irregular green patches which would someday be wings lay folded against his thorax. Long green ridges — the beginnings of antennae, of proboscis and of legs — ran half the length of his ventral side. Yellow bands and one snow white stripe encircled his fat green abdomen. His legs and his head had disappeared entirely, leaving him a defenseless thick green drop, but possessing a single intuitive skill — a skill to be used only once, and according to his dexterity in using it, Danaus in one moment would either live or die. Enclosed within his larval skin at the end of his abdomen, there was a black stalk, or cremaster, equipped with minute hooks which faced in all directions. He must remove this stalk from his skin and insert its hooks into the pearly button which he could neither see nor feel.

In order to accomplish this, he must support himself by grasping his dead skin between two segments of his spongy abdomen. Thus suspended, he must withdraw the stalk and, hanging virtually in mid-air, grope in the dark until he found the button of silk. His survival depended upon this one complicated maneuver, a culmination of the long ordeal of transforming from an independent free-moving animal into a state of vegetative immobility. Caterpillars which are weak or defective seldom complete this last difficult ecdysis with success. In the great plan of life, it is one of the many barriers which the strong surmount, leaving the weak behind.

When this extraordinary acrobatic feat had been executed, the green drop writhed and twisted violently until the cremaster was tightly hooked from all sides and the larval skin had been disengaged and dropped to the ground. Then it grew still. But in its stillness it was gradually changing form. In an hour the striped abdomen had become pale green and had shrunk to a third its original size, and the wings had expanded into two graceful triangles on which a faint tracery of veins could be discerned. Against the lowering sun, it had a glistening translucence, and it was still as with the stillness of death. . . .

For the first time in two weeks, the beam of Mr. Stevens' headlights swept across the Meadow. For two weeks he had been driving into town every morning at eight o'clock, combatting the noise and the exhaust fumes until he reached the underground garage a few city blocks from his office. Having parked his black sedan, he had walked these same blocks over the asphalt pavements and the cement sidewalks which had been whittled down from time to time to make room for more cars.

This short walk had been his only exercise of the day. For the rest, he had sat at his desk with figures running in and out of his head. Once in a while he had caught himself wondering about the use of living at all if there were no more to it than this, and longing to be in his cabin where he could forget the harsh thwack of heels hurrying across cement, the smell of pizzas and stale fried food and the sound of cheap music blaring from some obscure depth to mingle with the unremitting irritation of automotive engines clearing their throats.

But tonight all that was behind him. He unloaded the supplies which he had bought and made coffee which he drank sitting in the dark and looking out at the ghosts of trees which were cast on the ground by a full moon. It was very still, and he sat alone with his thoughts, allowing the stillness to settle over him until he felt himself immersed in a delicious loneliness. It was then that he saw the fox come cautiously out of his hole and trot away down the path. So it was the fox! He wondered with a kind of regret if his cherished feeling of loneliness would go away now that he knew his neighbor.

But if the fox was a neighbor, he was not a friend. He would never come running at a whistle. He would never wag his handsome bushy tail in a gesture of recognition. He would come out secretly in the silent dark. He knew things about the Meadow that Mr. Stevens would never know. He could trot into the tall grass and disappear as silently and completely as the green grass snake. He could find the pheasant's nest or the blackbird's nest, and he could find his obscure way home with no thought of a compass. In fact, it was really the fox's Meadow. Mr. Stevens owned it, but the fox was lord of it. Mr. Stevens could come in his jeep with his headlights and his noisy engine, or he could walk along the path in the morning, and not one creature would do more than give him a curious look. But when the fox came out of his den, he came out at night, stealthily and quietly and every creature in the Meadow knew that he came out to hunt. When the smell of the fox was in the air, the Meadow was curiously still.

Mr. Stevens felt a sudden pang of envy. He thought for a moment that he would give everything he had — his office and his shiny, black town car and his place in the world if he could only follow the fox — silently and in the dark of night — not with a flashlight but in the pale moonlight; not gropingly, not stumbling over every loose root and fallen branch — but trotting along in the world, in tune with the world — tuned to every little sound and the slightest of motions with no clock but the heat of the sun and the pull of the moon and the mysterious sensitive devices within his own body. This would really be freedom — freedom to live by his wits or freedom to die by his carelessness. To be owner of the Meadow was nothing. To be part of it was freedom, and he was not part of it. He lit his candle and spread out his sleeping bag on his folding army cot, vaguely resentful of even these small comforts.

Perhaps because he felt he was not part of the Meadow, Mr. Stevens suddenly realized that it was all the more valuable to him. He began to be aware of things he had looked at many times before but never actually seen. The aerodynamic skill of the bluejay in coordinating the muscles and feathers of his wings and tail as he lowered his clawed feet to come in for a landing; the provocative geometry of the spider's silver web, glittering with dew and sun; the superb economy of energy and motion in the goldfinch's flight pattern — these were things an engineer could understand, but engineer though he was, he had never noticed them before.

He found the place where he had pinched off the milkweed two weeks earlier, and he started across the Meadow in search of the redwing's nest, wading through waist-high greenness, the grass blades tickling his ankles and a cool dampness penetrating his comfortable old sneakers. He found the nest. In fact, the redwing himself, with his frantic screams and many up-and-down sorties actually showed him where it was. There were three small bobbing heads which consisted mainly of wide-open tangerine-colored beaks, and several wing bones about the size and color of match sticks. After this, since it was a warm sunny morning, he walked on, enjoying everything he saw.

The Meadow was filled with potential blossomings — the tight invisible buds of yarrow and fireweed, and the clusters of milkweed buds, not yet ready to open but already the color of half-ripe peaches.

There were two Danaids within sight of the path he walked. He saw the first, who, spending his last day as a caterpillar, had begun early to feed. Mr. Stevens did not know what it was that he saw, and his first impulse, as is often the case, was to kill such an ugly crawling thing. He had often killed similar creatures when he found them on his tomato plants at home, and he had burned whole nests of gypsy moth larvae, knowing full well what destruction they would cause if left unchecked. Such things were a detriment, or at best a nuisance, to all mankind. But in his Meadow, today was different. He stopped and watched the caterpillar as it shaved clean little strips from the edge of the leaf, and he felt a certain respect for such purposeful concentration. He walked on, wondering if it would be there, whatever it was, the next day. But the next day it would be gone, and however thoroughly he might search, he would not be able to find it. Possibly, in its last hours, the larva which had appeared so robust would succumb to the only disease known to attack its species* — a microbe which overnight could cause it to blacken and to die hanging by one pair of prolegs from the leaf on which it had sought to pupate. Perhaps, having pupated, the newly formed chrysalis would be eaten by a field mouse, or perhaps it would escape both fates, to hang silent and camouflaged in some adjacent place, as Danaus the son was already hanging.

Mr. Stevens did not see Danaus the son, hidden as he was against a background of spring green. He could not possibly have seen the discarded larval skin, which lay in the deep grass looking exactly like a dead fly. But Danaus

* *Micrococcus flaccidifex danai* (Brown). There is also a general bacteriosis caused by *Pseudomonas aeroginosa* (Miguel) sometimes found in Danaus plexippus, which is considered a potential insect pathogen. However, it has no invasive powers of its own, but will enter the hemocoel and cause a fatal septicemia if the insect has been weakened from other causes. It is most commonly found among insects reared under laboratory conditions.

had hung safely from his leaf all night, becoming gradually changed and perfected.

When the larva had begun to form within the egg, certain little groups of cells, belonging not to the larva but to the eventual butterfly, had also formed, and these had remained dormant, safely stored within the body of the caterpillar. Sometime after he had ceased to feed, these cells had awakened to life and begun to grow and multiply. Their presence had become dramatically evident during the six short minutes when the last larval skin had been shed, but before that they had been growing for a day and a night hidden beneath his skin. Now this morning the change from caterpillar to chrysalis was complete. Where once had hung a withered and dying larva, there was now a pendant of polished jade which seemed in no way related either to the larva or to the shapeless drop of the night before. The white stripe around its abdomen had disappeared and in its place there was a jet black band sprinkled with golden beads. On its glossy pale green surface was faintly etched the outline of the folded butterfly, inlaid with discs of gold. The purity of its contours, the balanced contrasts of its coloring, and the perfect symmetry of its design combined to make it an object of surpassing beauty.

V

Inside the Locked Room

(June 11–18)

O *world invisible, we view thee,*
O *world intangible, we touch thee,*
O *world unknowable, we know thee,*
Inapprehensible, we clutch thee!

FRANCIS THOMPSON

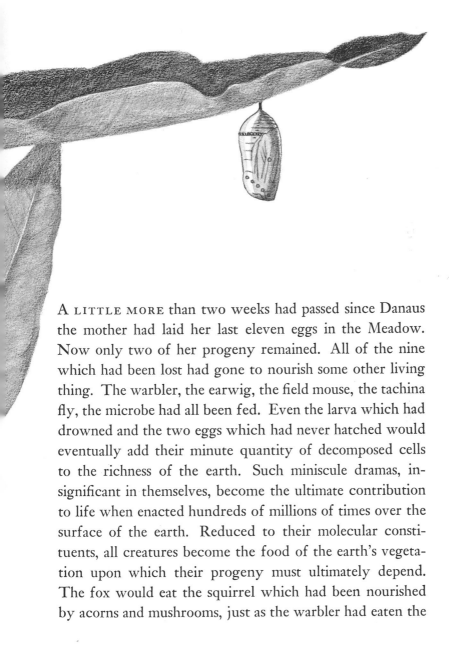

A LITTLE MORE than two weeks had passed since Danaus
the mother had laid her last eleven eggs in the Meadow.
Now only two of her progeny remained. All of the nine
which had been lost had gone to nourish some other living
thing. The warbler, the earwig, the field mouse, the tachina
fly, the microbe had all been fed. Even the larva which had
drowned and the two eggs which had never hatched would
eventually add their minute quantity of decomposed cells
to the richness of the earth. Such miniscule dramas, insignificant in themselves, become the ultimate contribution
to life when enacted hundreds of millions of times over the
surface of the earth. Reduced to their molecular consti-
tuents, all creatures become the food of the earth's vegetation upon which their progeny must ultimately depend.
The fox would eat the squirrel which had been nourished
by acorns and mushrooms, just as the warbler had eaten the

caterpillar which had lived on the leaves of the milkweed. And Mr. Stevens, when he cooked his steak over his charcoal grill, ate not only the steak, but the grasses of the Texas ranch and the corn of the plains on which the steer had been fattened.

On the way home from his exploration of the Meadow, Mr. Stevens saw Danaus. A fragment of sunlight struck his golden discs, and they sparkled for one brief moment. They could have been dew on a green bud, but by now the leaves were dry, and Mr. Stevens found himself unexpectedly confronting this jewel of the living world, hanging within reach of his hand. He reached out and felt of its cool quiescent perfection, and although it did not move, he knew that it was alive. He did not hear the faintest of sounds as he touched it — a barely audible click by which the chrysalis of Danaus, immobile though it may be, is able in some mysterious way to communicate with the mobile world; to send a signal from the depths of its dark helplessness — perhaps a warning heard and understood only by those small creatures which are alert from birth to every meadow sound. No one knows. The chrysalis looked like a Chinese ear drop, and he thought that his wife would have liked to own it. This thought reminded him of a day nearly five years before — the day of misery and helpless bewilderment when his world had turned to dust. He was aware once again of an emptiness which resignation had not yet filled, and a sadness that all beauty must be so transient.

But he studied the chrysalis for a long time with a feeling

of wonder. It was a perfect thing. Where had it come from? Where would it go? What was it for? The wonder of it seemed to him its greatest charm — more satisfying, perhaps, than the answers to his unspoken questions. His life was a huge volume of answers, facts and logic. Nothing was left unsolved any more. No one was satisfied until the last stone had been turned and the last creature flushed from his hiding-place. Life ought to be more than this. It ought to pay homage to the mysterious and the incomprehensible. There ought to be some sort of respect for things which had occurred all by themselves without help from people — things which people would never be able to duplicate even if they should learn the answers to all the questions. At that moment, the green chrysalis seemed more marvelous to him than all the bridges he would ever build over the highways, and contemplating it filled him momentarily with uneasiness and doubt. He left the chrysalis hanging from its leaf, but he kept the memory of it locked in his mind.

Over the huge span of time that is evolution, the four stages comprising the life of Danaus had been shaped, refined, and specialized so that the chance of his species' remaining alive was in almost perfect balance with nature. Each stage was assigned a special role in his total life cycle, and in the preservation of his species. In the egg he had been created from a single fertilized cell which had divided and multiplied and re-divided, the new cells migrating outward until a single layer of cells lay against the inside of the membrane which lined his chorion. This accomplished, the multiplying cells had formed little pockets of tissue which would become his internal organs and little protuberances that would develop into his walking prolegs and his mouthparts. Thus from a hollow ball of cells had been prepared all the elements necessary for his entire life cycle before he had left his shell.

As a caterpillar his function had been to eat and grow, until at length his original two millimeters had stretched to fifty, and his volume was a hundred thousand times what it had been when he first confronted the world. His appearance had protected him from some of his enemies, since the eyes of all animals do not see his bright tiger stripes as do human eyes; since the interplay of light and shadow filtering through the total greenness of spring blurs the outline of plant and animal alike, shifts and alters all of their multitudinous shades and hues; since his final size, his tonguelike filaments and his predisposition to strike suddenly as though to sting when disturbed, made him formidable to animals larger than he, even as a small snarling dog is a frightening thing to a man.

The chrysalis had evolved to protect the little creature during his long and complicated metamorphosis. It appeared to be an inanimate object, and indeed it could not move, but within its still body vast changes were taking place. These changes had begun in two tiny glands behind his brain which since his first day had been secreting microscopic amounts of a juvenile hormone. In these the wellspring had dried. These glands had controlled his larval growth, his larval life, and when their youth-giving substance had ceased to flow, Danaus the caterpillar had begun to die and the butterfly, to be formed.

First, as he had awaited his last ecdysis hanging head down from his leaf, Danaus had withdrawn his prolegs, as an airplane which had just left the ground retracts its landing gear. At the same time, the small wing patches which had been concealed *within* the body of the caterpillar, had turned themselves inside out like empty pockets and become cemented to the outside of the moist chrysalis which was beginning to form beneath the last larval skin. He had also severed his mouthparts, so that when this last skin finally shrank away these appendages altogether disappeared never to be seen again, and on the ventral side of the chrysalis where they had been there lay in thin converging lines the pulpy beginnings of the butterfly's long true legs, the long antennae replacing heretofore useless stubs, and the long proboscis which had once been the short maxillae used by the caterpillar to hold his food between his jaws.

The minute glands which five times had provided him with molting fluid, had begun to disappear. The marvelous spinning mechanism which had served him so well, providing him with enough silk for all his needs, was now outgrown, and it, too, had begun to wither away. But as these glands vanished, others were being formed. A gland at the tip of his abdomen would be capable of releasing a delicious perfume. His reproductive organs, which had existed only as a minute congregation of cells when he was a larva, were developing to maturity. Sperm cells were being produced by a complicated process which allowed each one only half as many chromosomes as the other cells in his body.

The stomach of the larva, equipped to digest massive quantities of pulverized milkweed leaves, had occupied more than three-fourths of his body cavity. The butterfly, whose meager subsistence would be the small amounts of nectar which he could suck from the depth of flowers, would require a stomach only a tenth this size. The principal muscles of the larva were located in his abdomen where they operated his walking prolegs and helped to digest his food. The butterfly would need no such muscles, but the marvelously powerful muscles being developed in his thorax would operate his huge wings, carrying him for hundreds of miles.

Sensory nerves would be planted in his antennae to give him direction and balance, and in his feet so that he could know the scent and taste of any object on which he might alight. The anal prolegs which had enabled him to suspend from his silken bead had been shed with his last larval skin, and in their place would appear a new organ which he would use to clasp the abdomen of his mate and hold her captive during mating. The forward part of his skeleton would lose its rubbery flexibility and become stiff and sclerotized — a support for his wings and a protection against collisions in mid-air — leaving only his abdomen soft and pliable. Minute hairs would grow on his body and scales on his wings, some colored with a fiery pigment, some structured to reflect parts of the sun's spectrum in a glowing iridescence. Velvet black, snowy white and fiery gold, his colors would be added last of all.

Inside the chrysalis, this marvelous transformation would be wrought invisibly in the space of only ten days. What forces sealed within its shell would effect such changes? What incomprehensible timing device would order them to begin? And how would Danaus himself know when they were accomplished — at what instant he would be ready to re-enter the world and lift his wings? Hanging head down in his tight little jade urn, how would he breathe? How would the degenerating organs of his larval life be discarded? What would nourish the growing butterfly?

In this limbo between one life and the next, without digestive system, without mouth, he could not feed himself. And yet, in order to achieve the miracle of metamorphosis, the absorption of air, the circulation of blood and the digestion of food must continue all during the time that the destruction and rebuilding of internal organs, of muscles, glands and nerves was taking place. The evanescent little creature so compactly cached away was not an embryo forming for the first time from undifferentiated cells. There were no yolk materials upon which he could feed as there had been within his egg. Nor would he be released from his prison a tiny infant as he had been from his egg, but as a perfect and complete adult, his growth attained, his instincts, his ability for self-protection and reproduction, his unexploited wisdom all at the peak of their perfection. His chrysalis would deprive him of his adolescence, for in it he must sleep out the period of transition between the child and the adult, which for most of the animals in the Meadow would be a time of excitement, frolic, merriment, and learning. Danaus would step suddenly from childhood to adult life, and he must cross the bridge between them while he slept. He would have no opportunity to gain wisdom and wile from his kind, but must rely on his instincts alone to guide him. The redwings in their snug nest hidden in the grass would be protected, taught and fed until they were as large as their solicitous parents. The squirrels deep in their tree hole, the chipmunks in their underground tunnel, the foxes in their den — all would be cared for, all would learn caution from the others in their den, all would enter the adult world armored with a knowledge of how to live in it. But Danaus would have to battle the world alone. Alone he had come into it, alone and unsheltered he had eaten his way to the chrysalis, and alone he would face the hazards of a new way of life, airborne into a world he had never seen. His only link with the world he had known would be his system of respiration, which would remain unchanged and intact throughout his entire existence. He would breathe as he had always breathed — not through lungs, for Danaus possessed no lungs. Air would enter his body through a series of spiracles, small openings in the sides of his abdomen. These spiracles had been situated in two rows along the sides of the larva. They could still be seen on the abdomen of the chrysalis, and would appear again on the abdomen of the butterfly. They were connected to minute tubes which branched and re-branched, growing ever smaller and more numerous until at length they delivered fresh air directly to every organ in his body without first sending it into his blood stream, and without benefit of lungs. The circulation of blood, also, would remain unchanged. Since he possessed no lungs, Danaus had no need for a complicated network of veins, arteries and capillaries such as that which connects the lungs of mammals with their circulatory systems. His blood would flow as it had always flowed. It would flow freely through his whole body, covering all his organs. From this open well within him, blood was drawn into a small tube which had its beginning near the end of his abdomen. It extended the length of his back, terminating in his head. His blood was pumped as water is pumped from a well. A series of small hearts in the abdominal section carried it through the tube in a steady stream, and it gushed out, fountainlike, into his head, whence it continued to stream over all his internal organs, keeping them moist, supplying them with food and collecting wastes, but taking no part in the transportation of air.

The devices which have been evolved by living things to bring them into harmony with their surroundings are often amazing, and the system by which Danaus respires, in its directness and simplicity, is not the least ingenious of these. Surely it must be one of the most successful, for all of the insects — which comprise most of the animal life on this earth — respire in the same manner.

But as he changed, how would he be fed? From egg to adult, nothing in his entire structure would change more radically than his digestive system. As a larva, he had fed continuously. As an adult, he would feed sparingly and sporadically. In his chrysalis, as in his egg, he was incapable, as an entity, of feeding himself. Protein had been available for his use in his egg, but only he himself existed within his chrysalis. The work of feeding him must be done by his own transparent emerald green blood which flowed without cease into every crevice and throughout all his parts. Present in it were infinitesimal components similar to white blood cells — the phagocytes — which must also be fed. The phagocytes would feed upon the decomposing organs of the larva, and the waste products of the phagocytes would become, in turn, the nourishment of the growing butterfly who would utilize nearly all of them. The insignificant wastes of the butterfly would be stored harmlessly within his body until he had emerged complete.

VI

Renaissance

(*June 18–19*)

For now we see through a glass, darkly;
but then face to face:
now I know in part; but then shall I know
even as also I am known.

I Corinthians 14:12

ON THE MORNING of the ninth day there was a blue shadow on his dorsal side, and by mid-afternoon the entire chrysalis of Danaus had become a rich teal blue. The antennae and proboscis and the legs of the butterfly were spread like a soft veil almost the entire length of his ventral side, and the triangles of his wings were washed with a faint salmon pink. The colors had begun to flow. All night long the chrysalis darkened, and by morning it had become a glistening black, obscuring the black band and the engraved outline on the outer surface of the shell. Only the golden discs remained, sparkling like jewels in the sun — and the stained glass windows that were wings shone orange on either side. The last molecules of pigment had been provided, and the last traces of liquid would soon be absorbed. It was the twentieth of June.

For the first time in ten days, Danaus moved of his own volition. The motion of his abdomen was tentative and brief and imperceptible, but slight as it was, it was enough to stretch the tight sheath which enclosed him, and all at once it seemed as though the region of the black band had sprung open — as though the cover of the urn had been lifted. But still there was no slightest stir, and for another half hour Danaus slept. Then the surface of the chrysalis began to be sprinkled with a silver frost which gradually spread to all its parts as Danaus loosened himself from his now dry covering. Still he did not move. Five minutes passed. Ten minutes. Then without further warning the shell began to crack — not where it had stretched, but at the point farthest from the leaf — at its utmost tip. Almost simultaneously seven fractures occurred at predetermined seams, as Danaus began to be born. He pressed against the cracking shell with his thorax and his head until the muscles of his wings were free, and then pushing with all his strength he freed them for another fraction of an inch. Now for the first time, Danaus, of the golden wings, could be seen to move through the transparent sheath of his chrysalis. With a series of convulsions he contracted his abdomen and managed to wrench it loose from the dried membranes which enmeshed it. Soft, spongy and fore-shortened, it tumbled out of the shell in a backward somer-sault, as if completely unattached to the rest of the insect, which was still inside the shell. A second later his wing tips, his proboscis, his antennae, burst forth in a sudden blossoming, and he was free, clinging with his hind legs to

the inner membrane of the chrysalis while with his fore-
legs he clawed desperately at the black band, now visible
once more. So rapidly did he begin to assume his final size
that within a fraction of a second, his body was twice as
large as his empty shell.

When he had assured himself that his grasp was secure,
Danaus ceased to struggle and rested quietly, swinging back
and forth in small semicircles. Weak, soft, and helpless, he
hung, waving his antennae and coiling and uncoiling the
two long halves of his proboscis in an effort to dovetail
their tiny notched edges into a single air-tight tube. If he
failed in this, he would be unable to drink, and in a few
days, he would become dehydrated and die.

At the same time he was working all of the muscles in
his body in order to stretch his abdomen and pump blood
into his finely pleated and still pliable wings, which in one-
half a minute had already tripled in size. All had happened
in complete silence but for the nearly inaudible crackling
of his clawed feet against the brittle surface of the shell.
The velvety body grew sleek and slender. The magnificent
wings unfolded, uncurled, flattened, and lay closed across
his back. Only the underside of his hind wings was visible
and they were of a pale coral hue edged with black and
white lace.

In less than eight minutes after the first crack had appeared in his chrysalis, Danaus had attained his full size —
his final shape. His legs still clung to his shell, and they
glistened sometimes jet black, sometimes steel blue, in the

sun as he was turned by the soft June wind. Because he possessed only four walking legs, he seemed more like an animal than an insect. It was only by careful study of his body at close range that his two front legs could be detected, folded uselessly against his thorax, living proof that his evolution was still in progress. At some point in the long history of his evolution he had become not merely a butterfly, but the specific kind of butterfly which is called a Danaid. He had become specialized by gradually discarding those parts of his life and his being which he no longer needed. He could walk, alight and balance himself on four legs as well as on six, and over the centuries he had practiced this habit until now his front legs, no longer necessary to him, were held folded, unused, but in no way an encumbrance. In another hundred thousand years, they would perhaps perform some new function, like all of his mouth parts, which had once been legs. In the dark recesses of his origin, his palpi, his chewing mandibles, and the maxillae of the larva which had now become his long proboscis — perhaps even his slender clubbed antennae — had once served him as legs, and he had crawled over the earth absorbing his nourishment through an aperture somewhere in his head.

As he hung from the underside of his leaf, his folded wings were almost the color of the milkweed blossom above him, but his pointed palpi, meeting in the middle of his face, rose like a black and white crown over the top of his head, matching the colors with which his body was clothed. Although his wings, expanded to their full size, were as flat as the leaves of the aspen, their membranes were still limp and soft like wet tissue paper, and their black veins as resilient as a willow twig in the wind. It would be another hour before he could fly, and until then he must remain helpless and vulnerable, as he had been each time his skin had been shed. He hung waiting for his full strength, and as he waited, four red drops fell to the ground from the end of his abdomen — the wastes of his metamorphosis — the last link in the forging of his life chain — his parting gift to the earth as he became a creature of the air.

Presently he left his shell and walked cautiously along his leaf to the stem of the plant. He climbed up for several inches to a leaf where the sun would fall on his wings, warming them until they dried. Tentatively he opened and closed them a crack, testing their muscles.

Sitting on a dead branch the phoebe had watched him. She had seen him climb the stem of his plant, and she could see him now, but his wings were pointed exactly in her direction, so that only their edges and not their coral scales were visible to her. All she really saw were his legs and the outline of his body. Four young phoebes needed to be fed. She had caught endless insects for them, but they were never satisfied. She eyed this large enticing morsel, and then she swooped down upon it, her beak open.

Danaus, the Golden One, could neither roll from his leaf nor deliver a frightening stab in her direction. His larval defenses were gone, and without experience or knowledge, he must use his present equipment to defend himself. He had seen the phoebe coming with his wonderful new eyes, and as she was about to devour him, his instinct told him to spread his wings. In a flash, two tongues of flame shot out from his body, and instantly he was a hundred times larger and more vivid than the phoebe had suspected. She wheeled and fled in terror.

The Meadow was still with the torpor of mid-day. There was a lull in the scampering of animals, but not all of the Meadow's inhabitants were as debilitated by the heat as they. The insects came alive under the sun's warmth, and the smallest of sounds now filled the air — the hum of bees and the buzz of flies. One flicker began the crescendo of his mechanical laugh and then let it fade away. A brown toad squatted in the grass by the path's edge, his legs grotesquely bowed, his half-closed eyes cushioned by his warty brow. He appeared to be asleep, but he could hear the buzzing all around him, and he waited. Suddenly, in that fraction of a second which is too short to be seen, his hinged tongue lashed out and in, and a tachina fly which had settled on the path to rest in the sun was gone.

The milkweed was in bloom, and its rich heavy fragrance spread across the Meadow, luring the honey bee away from the clover and the sulphur butterflies from the air where they had been spiraling like tiny yellow whirlwinds, each trying to determine the sex of the other. For a moment, the bee hovered over the pink ball of flowers, and then sank his tongue deep into its heart. He drank with relish, but so greedy did he become that in his haste he thrust his tongue into a narrow slit in the flower's pollen gland, and from this trap he could not escape. He beat the flower frantically with his feet and made miniature siren alarms with his racing wings, but his struggling only worsened his plight, and in the end it was the phoebe who, with her sharp eyes, saw him and with her sharp beak pulled him free.

For nearly a month the overwintering swallowtails had gradually been emerging and mating and dotting the young Queen Anne's lace and wild parsnip with their round yellow eggs, which were completely hidden from view among the curling points of the plant's leaves. The newly hatched larvae were feeding apparently without fear on the sunny side of the plant, and they so closely resembled the droppings of birds that the birds themselves did not deign to consider them as food. The earliest of these larvae had long since retired into the darkness of their chrysalids and now the season's first new generation of butterflies was beginning to appear in the Meadow. Their favorite nectar was in the blossoms of lilac, but by now these had all faded away, and the black swallowtail, polyxenes, searching for other sources of nourishment, fluttered across the Meadow scarcely a foot above the tips of the tall grasses, her path a random zig-zag. The paucity of small creamy moons bordering her wings bespoke her sex, while the smooth sheen of her forewings and the glittering blue spangles of her hind wings proclaimed her newness. She had emerged only the day before, and not yet having mated, she pursued her irresponsible quest for nectar unhampered by the problems of egg laying. As she approached the milkweed stalk of Danaus, her dark cloak cast more than five thousand images upon those lenses of his eyes which were focused in her direction, and once more he spread his glistening wings — but this time he sprang from his leaf, and in one superb moment he was free of the earth. He lurched through the air in astonished uncertainty, then wheeled and flew to a branch of the nearest tree. He was free of the earth at last. The long desperate struggle was over, and the long night past. Red of the firebrand and gold of the sun were fused in the fiery wings he presented to the noon-day sun, and a delicious fragrance — sweet and spicy and erotic — was diffused across his back. His wings and his body were filled with power and he was free. He leapt high in the air and encircled the field, gliding, dipping, soar-ing, surveying from his place in the sky a world of leaves which he had already forgotten.

Insects have inhabited the earth for about 340,000,000 years, by virtue of their ability to adapt successfully not only to their surroundings, but to the interminable, pitiless, unpredictable, universal onslaught of evolution. Certain species of insects which, in evolving, became too large, eventually perished, for the relatively fragile exoskeleton of an insect is like a balloon filled with water. There is no inner framework for the support of tissue. Many smaller species have survived, helped by their smallness to conceal themselves from their enemies. They live out their little lives, often producing several generations in a season, and each generation produces a vast number of eggs. The pair of redwings, rearing two broods, would lay no more than eight eggs in a season, and of these perhaps half would survive. But in the same summer Danaus the mother was the matriarch of not two broods, but of three generations, and if only one tenth of the eggs of each generation should reach maturity, she would still have been responsible for the existence or 160,000 living descendants.

The length of time which had elapsed since the appearance on earth of the first known primeval butterfly was perhaps 50,000,000 years, but long before that its original ancestor had been some lowly segmented worm which had exhibited its talent for adjusting to change by growing legs and crawling out onto the surface of the earth instead of slithering through its dark interior on his belly. For the miraculously complex organism that was Danaus, with his superbly efficient and specialized stages of development, his subtle defenses, his skills and protective devices, his diverse instincts, and his completely functional beauty — for such a superlative creature to evolve from this meager beginning — had required perhaps a billion years.

VII

Staking Out a Claim
(June 19–21)

Out of the night that covers me,
  Black as the Pit from pole to pole,
I thank whatever gods may be
  For my unconquerable soul.

W. E. HENLEY

DANAUS SURVEYED the Meadow and he was attuned to what he found there. He would stay until his mate came. Here his life would reach its apex, and by forging his one small but vital link in the great chain of evolution, he would give to his species the assurance of continued life, and the possibility of immortality. He would prepare for the coming of this other butterfly with whom he should mate. He flew over and around the Meadow, drinking from the flowers and sensing the direction of wind and sun, locating the stands of milkweed, the nearness of trees, and he ensconced himself in a part of the Meadow which would be his.

In much the same way, the redwing had established a territory for himself when he had first arrived at the Meadow, and in much the same way, the squirrel had fought for his oak tree, although his battle had not been a difficult one, since even the starling had no wish to share the tree with such a formidable threat to his family. In much the same way the meadowlark had routed every other bird from his end of the Meadow, relegating both redwing and pheasant to places on the opposite side of the path, and staking out an entire acre for himself where he could construct elaborate grass tunnels leading to his hidden nest, and where he could partake undisturbed of an abundance of grasshoppers and caterpillars.

Everything would be in readiness when she arrived. Danaus flew back and forth and across his chosen ground with swift powerful strokes of his magnificent wings and finally came to rest invisibly in the midst of it. Soon three sulphur butterflies spiraled across the Meadow in their usual quest for information. Although they flew behind him, Danaus saw their interwoven images through his bulging insect eyes which were so constructed that he could detect the slightest motion coming from any direction. He rose from his hidden lookout and started in pursuit, scattering the intruders in a few moments. Again he perched motionless, watching. His compound eyes provided him with a sweeping hemisphere of interlocking images, encompassing all the territory above and around him for a distance of perhaps twenty feet — a staggering vista, especially in comparison to what he had seen with his larval eyes. As a larva, he had barely been able to distinguish light from darkness. He had been able to detect no motion and only the vaguest of contours. Of all the changes which had revolutionized his way of life, none was more amazing than that which had replaced the three beady little spots on the sides of his larval head with his present compound insect eyes — a lens system typifying the most elaborate and complex organs of sight in the entire animal kingdom.

The eyes of Danaus the larva had each contained a single lens, as did the eyes of the fox, the redwing, and the other birds and animals of the Meadow. When he emerged from his chrysalis, each eye of Danaus contained 6000 lenses. Underneath each lens there was a crystal cone which collected the entering light and sent it to six long triangular rods — the retinulae — the organs with which he *perceived* the light. From here it was transmitted through a complex of membranes, fibers and nerves to a region of his brain which translated it into sight.

Each crystal cone with its encasing retinulae was surrounded by a cloak of pigment cells. The function of these was to *mask* the entering light so that only a very thin band of direct light could pass, while all oblique light was excluded. Thus a vast number of minute separate images were created, and they converged upon a still more minute area of his brain.

From the eyes of a man, an animal or a bird, two images are sent to his brain. From the two eyes of Danaus, there were 72,000. When Mr. Stevens had seen the smooth larva of Danaus, one image had been received by each of his two eyes, and in his brain, they had merged into a single image so that he saw but one perfect larva. In the two eyes of

Danaus, 72,000 images, each a tiny pinpoint, were received, but only Danaus himself knew the secret of what he saw. Perhaps in his brain the images were fused into one broad panoramic world. Perhaps he saw a huge mosaic of images, each slightly different from those adjoining it. Or perhaps in the delicate nerve center which translated the images it received into sight, there was some unidentified biological device resembling an electronic scanner which moved across his visual center with lightning rapidity, turning the 72,000 images he saw into one.

Danaus did not remember that once long ago he had been compelled to roll from a leaf and find shelter under the grass in order to avoid capture by the redwing, but even if he had remembered, it would have made no difference now. In those days, his only instinct had been caution and the preservation of his own life. Now it made no difference that the redwing measured nine inches in length while the body of Danaus had actually shrunk since his larval days and now measured but an inch and a half. Now in the fullness of his virility, no obstacle was too great, and no adversary too dangerous for him to face, and when the redwing — in size and strength a giant by comparison — flew across the boundary of his estate in search of food, Danaus shot into the air with all the speed and ferocity his whole eighth of an ounce of being could muster.

A warning noise might have been less terrifying to the redwing — the staccato transmitter of a sparrow or the angry squawk of a pheasant — these bird sounds he could have understood — or even the whine of an attacking hornet. But he was conscious only of a blazing fury nearly half his size which had suddenly appeared from nowhere and was bearing down upon him with fierce determination and accuracy — a huge soundless thing which was certainly no bird, was flying to attack him. Who his enemy was, or what he had done to merit such an attack, he did not know, nor was he curious to find out. The feathers of his wings splashed out as he broke his flight in mid-air, and retreated in confusion from two pairs of tissue-thin wings and a fragile body no larger than his own beak. The redwing was defeated — not by the wings of the eagle, but by the wings of Psyche*. Danaus had won his first victory over him by strategy and his second by reckless courage. Against so powerful an adversary, only such victories were possible since, frail as he was by comparison and having neither sting nor tooth nor talon, he could never have hoped to win a victory by strength or arms. This knowledge would have caused great chagrin to the redwing (as it has to many a general during the course of history), but he would never know, and Danaus, as long as he remained in the Meadow, would continue to out-maneuver him.

On the twenty-first of May, the mother of Danaus had arrived at the Meadow from South Carolina. She had been among the first of the Monarchs to reach New England, but others were not far behind. All of the Monarchs,

* The Goddess Psyche, identified with the human spirit, soul or mind, is usually depicted with the wings of a butterfly.

whether they had passed the cold months in scattered groups or in huge congregations, had begun to migrate. From their southernmost winter habitats in California, in Mexico, Texas, and along the Gulf coast to Florida, they had all felt the same restless urge to fly north.

In the largest colony in Florida, the Monarchs had lived out the winter in a grove of live oaks, clustered by the thousands in the branches of the trees. As closely packed together as unpicked dates, and indeed looking somewhat like them from a distance, they had clung immobile to the slender leaves most of the winter, dropping down only occasionally to feed in the mid-day sun. Then toward the end of February, they had departed as unexpectedly as they had come, and suddenly the branches which had drooped with their weight were empty. All had obeyed the same awakening impulse, and within a week, out of the thousands which had lived in the grove since the previous November, not one remained.

The females who had mated were the first to leave. They left a few at a time, each flying in a northerly direction, independent of all the others, each seeking milkweed in sufficient supply to nourish all of her young.

And the other thousands of Monarchs in the colony had followed close upon the heels of their departure and spread out across the spring, sowing the tenuous seeds which would cause all the gardens and meadows east of the Appalachian range to blossom with life and motion and colored wings.

But what had induced them to leave? Since they could

neither reason nor decide, but only sense and perceive, what forces had interacted to ignite the explosion of their departure? Perhaps when the first few had left, the rest had followed these leaders in a kind of hysterical mass exodus whether they had mated or not. Or perhaps each individual butterfly had flown at the moment — and only at the moment — when his particular being had been fired with the urgency to fly.

But whether the sudden emigration of the colony from the live oak grove had been caused by hysteria or by urgency, some far more profound biological change had surely preceded the immediate cause. Some delicate shifting in the composition of each individual insect — an altering of his own peculiar rate of metabolism, the balance of his hormones, the division of his chromosomes — perhaps an admixture of all these had kindled his restlessness.

And these inner changes must in turn have been set in motion by some equally mysterious combination of outward circumstances — some coalescence of heat and humidity, of tidal rhythms and barometric pressures, of the quality and quantity of the sun's rays, of visible and invisible light. Somewhere in this unfathomable spiral of changing conditions lay the spark which had touched each individual member of the colony and awakened in him the irrepressible desire to leave the live oak grove forever and travel north.

When the emigration had begun, the first female to leave the colony had flown directly north by northeast in search of a place to lay her eggs. She had not stopped to feed, but had lived upon the fat which was stored in her body. Like the mother of Danaus, she had traveled only during the time of warm sun. She had traveled alone, and alone she had faced all the hazards from which she had been protected by the colony. As she approached the one crowning achievement of her life — the laying of her eggs — she had returned to the solitary existence into which she had been born, and which had been hers until the great mass migration of the previous autumn had made her a part of the colony. She had withstood the rain and the cold and the dark, and her faded wings matched the pale light and faint warmth of the March sun. Finally, in the pasturelands of Virginia she had found the first tender shoots of milkweed, and there she laid her eggs and died.

Her offspring grew, and by the end of April, had become butterflies, and they too had mated and dispersed and one of these, continuing the northern voyage to Ontario, had reached New England toward the end of May. In a field not far from the Meadow, she had paused just long enough to deposit three eggs before forging on, and of these three eggs, one would live to become the mate of Danaus.

VIII

The Pinnacle
(June 19–28)

> *Non v'accorg etveoi, che siam vermi*
> *nati a formar l'angelica farfalla,*
> *che vola alla giustizia senza schermi?*
>
> *Do you not perceive that we are worms*
> *Born to form the angelic butterfly*
> *Which flies to judgement without defense?*
>
> DANTE

THE SPARK OF LIFE in this one egg grew and hatched
and transformed and in a little less than three weeks the
sleeping butterfly which was destined to be the mate of
Danaus was ready to emerge. On the nineteenth of June
when she shattered her glassy cage and plunged headlong
into the world, she awoke to find herself suspended from
the only stalk of milkweed in a blackberry patch. Suddenly
she was alive in this warm sweet world with the buzzing
of bees all around her and the images of bees — multiplied
a thousandfold — in and out of her eyes like tiny darts, but
she immediately became so engrossed in the pressing task
of dilating her wings that she did not notice them, while
they, in turn, were so engrossed in gathering nectar that
they paid no attention whatever to the fact that a new
creature had just toppled into the world right beside them.
Eight minutes later her closed wings, although still soft and
a little puffy, like partly baked cookies, had attained their
full size, and, while they were thus folded, she looked
exactly like Danaus in every respect except for one small
detail. On each of his hindwings there was a faint

shadow touching the branching vein called cubitus, and on hers this was missing. She remained in the shade of her leaf until late afternoon, and then flew for the first time — to a tall tree where she could spend the night in safety.

It was on the morning of the third day after Danaus had established the boundaries of his estate that she came. She sailed into the Meadow with casual grace, gliding easily onto a blossom which she explored with her long black tongue. Two or three full strokes of her wings lifted her to a height from which she could again glide in a long descending arc. From tip to tip, her forewings measured more than five and a half inches. They were long and tapering and delicately curved, and the thick costal veins which supported them were heavily scaled with black. These veins, strong and durable as they were, would be considered frail by any standards except those pertaining to a butterfly. While hanging from her chrysalis, she had pumped blood into them from her body, and they had expanded, but later when they had hardened and dried she had recalled the blood, leaving the wing veins a series of hollow tubes, light, buoyant and very brittle. These wings with their seemingly tireless muscles could carry her as far as eighty miles in a single day — farther if she flew before a strong wind.

She skimmed easily above the tops of the meadow flowers, using her round and much less rigid hindwings to steady herself — to balance and help direct her flight — and finally she flew across the property of Danaus, and seeing that she had come, he rose to meet her.

He flew with none of his former belligerent determination, but fluttered into the air and glided over and around the flower upon which she was feeding. Seeing that he was unable to penetrate her indifference, he darted close and touched her wings, and she was conscious of a fragrance which she had never perceived before — sweet and spicy and erotic. Then the chase began — triangles of flight making a crazy quilt of wings and sun; sparks of burning gold — essence of joy — then high in the air above the trees, above the world in a long double helix which broke apart as they descended onto the branch of an elm tree. Of such primitive patterns is woven the fabric of life — which has no end. . . .

The sun caught the glorious burnished copper of her forewings which were crossed and edged with jet black veins — the pale gold of her hindwings, and the bold black and white scallops on their circumference. She rested on the branch fanning them, and Danaus fluttered over and above and around her. From the scent gland in the end of his abdomen, he had spilled his perfume into two small black pockets touching the vein cubitus on the surface of his hindwings, and there it had been trapped by a wax-like substance which released it slowly, so that it diffused and filled the air through which his wings were vibrating and filled the consciousness of his mate, hypnotizing her with its fragrance — and her wings trembled as she waited. Now in one sudden instant, he grasped her abdomen between his claspers and they mated. For a while they rested and all was motionless save for the ebb and flow of their wings — save for the ecstasy of life and the shimmering hot white sun. . . .

Some time later a crow, not even aware of their presence, settled on the limb with a thud and a loud CAW! and the startled Danaus rose from his perch with his mate beneath him. Now he knew his full potency — the full strength of his extraordinary wings. With great sweeping strokes he carried her half the length of the Meadow and back, testing his endurance, sensing his power, and alighting finally on the tip of a tall mullein plant.

Mr. Stevens was spending a long weekend at his cabin. He had been trimming dead branches from the trees around his door, sawing them into lengths and stacking them for firewood. He was very tired. He needed the recuperative tonic of solitude, for his week had been miserable. His estimators had finally been pressured into finishing the bids on the new highway, and he had spent three days checking out their figures. Now he found himself wishing he would lose the contract. . . . Two hundred families to be dispossessed — seven farms to lose between a hundred feet and two acres of land each — a city to be dissected — a marsh to be filled in and trees to be felled — eleven new bridges — a six-lane highway with room for a thousand more cars an hour — cement mixers — bulldozers — unions — coffee breaks — pneumatic drills — dollars and cents — dollars and cents — the Mayor cuts the ribbon and VROOOOOM! . . .

When the logs were all neatly stacked, he went into the

kitchen where he made a sandwich and drank two cups of coffee. Then he sat on his little porch for a while, smoking his pipe and watching two half-grown squirrels tumbling on the ground in mock battle. He felt imbued with self-sufficiency. This was the way to live. Why not just bow out of the mad race to accumulate more and more things. What did he need any more money for, anyhow? Where was the meaning in all of it? The two small squirrels chasing each other through his trees counted for more than he did. They would grow up and reproduce, eat and be eaten, and in doing so make their required contribution to the magnificent panorama of life which had been in the building for so many millions of years; while he, on a grandiose scale which no one could possibly overlook, continued to destroy it.

After carefully knocking the ashes from his pipe into an empty tin can reserved for the purpose, he wandered away from the cabin, taking no predetermined route but walking wherever the contours of the ground beneath his feet led him. Three times as he made his circuitous way among the ferns and brambles he passed a tree upon which a newly emerged mourning cloak was drying its wings, but they so perfectly matched the trees upon which they were resting that he did not see any of them. He did see two others flying silently among the trees, and the day before there had been one resting on a shingle of his cabin, taking advantage of a little patch of sunshine. He did not know that these three had been part of 200 eggs laid on the willow tree at the edge of his Meadow a month earlier. The little larvae had hatched and constructed for themselves a silken cradle to which they returned each night after feeding, and inside of which they had molted for the first time. After this they had moved to a new twig, leaving their discarded skins behind them. They had stayed together in a bristling black colony all during their larval life, and their numbers had protected them from predators. Only occasionally when one had become separated from the group had a small bird swooped down and snapped up the straggler. At each molting the skins had been left on a twig of the branch — stiff little black ghosts of the larvae themselves, still and grisly sentinels, unkowingly guarding the tree, and the larvae which had deserted them.

By the time there were four groups of such skins on various branchlets, the larvae had become spiked and silvery gray with scarlet prolegs and a scarlet stripe along their backs. They continued to feed in tight little clusters on the same stem of leaves, which made them appear enormous and forbidding, and they were left undisturbed. The willow tree was very large. The small branch on which they had spent their lives was now wholly defoliated. Mr. Stevens was not aware that for the privilege of having twelve exquisite butterflies in his woodlot, the only price he had paid was the foliage on a four foot branch of willow. The branch was not dead, only temporarily bare. New leaves would soon sprout again. In the opulence of his Meadow he had never missed the leaves, and it made no difference to anyone that they were gone.

One sunny day the full grown larvae had started down

the trunk of the tree in close procession. When they reached the ground, they separated for the first time, and each embarked on a perilous journey alone. Those which had been parasitized earlier by the tachina fly perished. Others succumbed to other pitfalls, but twenty survived, and each pupated on a different tree. By this time they were scattered over an area which covered more than four acres. As pupae they all matched the color of the trees to which they had attached themselves and, being thus disguised, twelve of the twenty escaped the sharp eyes of squirrels and birds and these all emerged within twenty-four hours of each other.

After tramping around in the woods for a while, Mr. Stevens altered his course and came out into the Meadow — where the mosquitoes were waiting to attack his neck and ears and the wood ticks were waiting for the privilege of crawling onto the cuffs of his trousers. It just wasn't his day. He had better go back to the cabin before falling into some woodchuck's hole and breaking a leg. He turned toward the path, waving off the mosquitoes and wondering if this was going to be the day he stepped on a hornet's nest. Presently he thought he saw a tall tiger lily growing about thirty feet ahead of him . . . no, not a tiger lily. It had four petals like some sort of big four-pointed gold star . . . no, not a star, either. It was a butterfly. He reached out to catch it, and it darted away. A double butterfly! In fact, Siamese twin butterflies was what it looked like. He followed them with his eyes until they settled on a dead

branch several feet above his head; and as he stood watching them, it suddenly occurred to him that they were
mating. Somehow this knowledge revived his spirits. The
tenacity of life! Not just the individual will to live, like a
fox running from the hounds, but the actual tenacity of
life itself. You could kill off a species all right, but you
couldn't kill *life*, because here it was, being renewed, and
it was always being renewed somewhere — sweeping ahead
in spite of all the inroads people like him had made by
chopping up the country . . . Well, at least he hadn't
destroyed the Meadow. And he hadn't even killed anything but a mosquito — not even that big striped caterpillar
he had seen the last time he was in the Meadow; and what,
after all, did a caterpillar amount to? But it was alive, and
that must be for something.

His wood-chopping and his walk in the hot sun had
made him pleasantly tired, so after an early supper he read
for a while by the light of his lantern and then went to
sleep. He didn't know what time it was when he awoke
in the night, but it was very dark, and the light of the half
moon was falling through the trees and sending faint white
fingers across his window pane. He was vaguely conscious
that he had heard an unfamiliar sound, and he lay very
still and listened. There it came again — a strange sort of
soft falsetto growl. He crept from his cot in the dark and
felt his way to the window. At first he saw nothing, but
when he had separated the familiar objects in the dooryard
from the camouflaging shadows, he could see the outline
of the well and the moss-covered log behind it, and very

faintly he could see the beginning of the path. There was
not a breath of wind, but something was moving. . . .

The foxes had come out of their den. The mother, thin,
exhausted, and moth-eaten, lay beside the log watching —
guarding. And the young foxes were scampering over and
around her, over the acoustical carpet of pine needles, over
the log, around the well, leaping at each other, rolling
themselves into balls of yellow fur, dancing in the moonlight. They stood poised for battle, and their sharp furry
heads were like three-spiked halberds. They bared their
little teeth at one another and plastered down their over-
sized triangular ears, feigning ferocity, and the white tips
of their tails bounced between the shadows like ping-pong

balls. They made hardly a sound, but for that same sub-
dued falsetto growl. Mr. Stevens, his eyes having grown
accustomed to the dark, could follow the gyrations of their
small supple bodies, and he knew who they were.

Then the Lord Fox came trotting up the path from the
Meadow carrying a prize almost as large as he. Its long
curling tail feathers dragged between his feet. Its brave,
red head, sightless now, wobbled and drooped from its
white-ringed neck. He dropped the pheasant on the ground
in front of his mate, and they all fell upon it, gnashing and
gnawing, tearing it apart, devouring the flesh and crunch-
ing the marrow out of the bones, until nothing remained of
it but the long curling tail and a heap of carnival-colored
feathers.

The union of Danaus and his mate endured for seven
hours, during which time he deposited within her body an
opalescent wax-like envelope containing enough sperm —
much more than enough — to fertilize all the eggs she
would ever lay. And at the end of the seventh hour it was
nearing dusk, and Danaus relaxed his grasp on her abdomen
so that they separated. They did not fly but remained on
the same limb overnight and until the sun rising over the
border of trees fell upon their wings and upon the blossoming Meadow. Then they drank of the nectar and parted
into their own separate worlds — he to the pollenization
of flowers — she to the propagation of her race. The
Meadow was lush with milkweed in full blossom. Hers
was a festival of recrudescence — his an orgy of drinking.

She remained in the Meadow for two days and two nights, and in all she deposited 183 eggs, of which twenty lived to become the third generation of Danaids in the Meadow that summer. After this, she continued northward, mostly without pausing to feed, laying eggs along the way as her mother had done, until she reached a small clearing filled with milkweed on the island of Islesboro in Maine, and here she died. In all, she had laid 717 eggs, and the last twenty or more of these were laid on the island in Maine.

Danaus remained in the Meadow for a day. So absorbed had he been in finding a mate that he had scarcely taken time to feed, and now he must satisfy his hunger and his thirst. There was still a certain amount of fat in his body which had been accumulated during his larval life, but water, at least, he must have. During humid or rainy weather — days when it was not his habit to fly, he could accumulate moisture through his spiracles which delivered air directly to his organs, but the weather had been unusually dry, and for four nights not even dew had fallen on the grasses. There was plenty of nectar in the milkweed to meet his immediate needs, and the next morning after he had left the Meadow, he found gardens in which the flowers, having been watered the night before, still held small amounts of moisture among their petals. This he drank along with the nectar of the flowers. His long proboscis probing the depths in search of nectar rubbed against the anthers of each blossom, and soon became coated with yellow powder which he then unwittingly transferred to the stigma of the next blossom and the next in a long series of pollenizations without which the flowers could have produced no seeds. Sometimes he stopped to clean his proboscis with his feet, and these, too, carried pollen to other blossoms — lemon lilies and oriental poppies, veronica and primrose — each flower accepting only that minute golden grain of the powder of life which would allow it to reproduce in kind when its full seeds should fall upon the ground.

From time to time Danaus returned to the Meadow, but these times became less frequent as his rather haphazard circumnavigations carried him slowly north, and finally after a week he was seen there no longer. His flight had become gradually less circuitous until he was following a generally northerly but still irregular path.

IX

The Northern Voyage
of Danaus
(June 28–July 15)

From this hour I ordain myself loosed of limits and
    imaginary lines,
Going where I list, my own master total and absolute . . .

WALT WHITMAN

IT WAS on the twenty-eighth day of June that Danaus circled across the end of the Meadow for the last time. For a week he had flown, fed, and basked in the sun. His long black abdomen was sleek with stored fat and because he flew with consummate skill and finesse, his enormous wings still kept their golden sheen. He glided with leisurely assurance until he arrived at the border of trees around the Meadow, and then, lifting himself high above them, he disappeared from sight.

A few days after he left the Meadow, Danaus mated a second time. He was living in a year of many Monarchs, and wherever there was milkweed, their eggs had been laid and other Monarchs were flying. The year before, there

had been few, and for four years before that. Now suddenly they were everywhere, and there would be many again for perhaps two years to come. Their ebb and flow would be determined as it had always been, by the receding or augmenting numbers of other species in a long line of fluctuations, and this chain was governed by the complex fabric of the weather which one year shed its munificence upon one form of life and the next upon another. And so the prevalence of each species vacillates in its turn, and the excessive diminution of the most insignificant bacteria or the meanest weed can threaten the food supply of another species, initiating a disastrous pyramid until one day, perhaps years later, a swarm of locusts, their numbers unchecked by the presence of their usual predators, may destroy the grain upon which thousands of men or cattle are dependent for their lives; or until the gypsy moths may destroy a hundred acres of apple orchard because the tachina flies had failed to appear in sufficient numbers the year before. So it is that in some years the grapes of France make superb wines — in other years only mediocre; that in some years the lilacs cover the trees almost to the ground while in others there are only meager tassels of bloom; that in some years the Monarchs appear by the thousands over all the land, and in other years the gardens are devoid of their wings.

In all, Danaus mated four times. Of the 1700 eggs which were fertilized by his sperm, seventy-five lived to complete the metamorphosis which made them butterflies.

Taking a course which was generally north and west, Danaus soon reached unfamiliar territory, and a hazard which he had never encountered before — the superhighway.

The meadows and marshes and billowing hillsides of New England no longer followed each other in an uninterrupted panorama as they had done in the days of his ancestors. In fact, many of their original contours no longer existed. Hills had been leveled, marshes filled, cliffs blasted away, and the wounds had been bandaged with great rolls of cement, winding around and through them in an interminable tangle. And over it all, the cars racing back and forth like ants over carrion created false winds, and the sun flashing back from their windows created false light. Danaus flew into this terrifying maelstrom for the first time at a junction of highways where five converging routes gained access to each other at a huge rotary, made still more populous by a motel, a restaurant, and a garage between the various entering highways, and a nearby airport which spat out and sucked in aircraft from low altitudes like some mammoth invisible toad. Before he was aware of the danger, Danaus found himself in the midst of it. He flew frantically back and forth trying to escape, but all his skills and all his wiles were of no use in this false and unnatural situation. He was tossed between the conflicting currents of air like a scrap of paper until at length an updraft enabled him to rise almost vertically for twenty feet or more and he escaped, miraculously without damage to his wings. He was more fortunate in his escape than many of his tribe, for in this year of the abundance of insects, at all the stopping places on all the highways of New England — the toll gates, the traffic lights, the picnic areas — the roadside was littered with dead butterflies which had been trapped in the radiator grilles of fast-moving vehicles and had fallen to the ground only when the cars came to a halt.

Having made his escape, Danaus continued along the edge of the highway, flying west for a while but eventually turning north once more into a country village filled with gardens and surrounded by fields, and here he roosted until morning. When the sun had warmed his wings, he sallied forth to explore his surroundings, feeding, resting, and in tune with the territory he had found.

Toward noon he came to a garden bordered with nasturtiums, and he fluttered close to the ground among them, a living part of their color. He was engaged in the mutually beneficial task of feeding upon their nectar and pollenating their blossoms when a ruby-throated hummingbird roared into his delicate and tranquil world. He had often given chase to larger birds. This time he seemed the equal of his adversary in size. With a few menacing flashes of his great wings, he darted toward the bird, but veered away a second before the point of contact was reached. A lightning swift encounter ensued which slashed through the garden in short, jagged streaks. There was a series of parries and feints, stabs and thrusts — an emerald meteor — a flash of fire. In ten seconds it was over without either having touched the other, and the ruby-throat, summoning only a fraction of his superior speed and power, shot over the rooftop, rising in a perfect arc which left Danaus in possession of the garden — a victor without glory.

It was a needless retreat for the hummingbird. He was superior to Danaus not only in speed and power, but in almost every respect. He was far more compactly built, and structurally he was more sound. He was less vulnerable, and he possessed effective weapons. With one stroke of his beak or one grip of his claws, he could have disabled the butterfly forever, while Danaus was unarmed and incapable of removing a single feather from the skin of the bird. His only weapons were his defenses. In a short flight he could outmaneuver the hummingbird, whether chasing or chased, and his wings in the sun were like living coals. His tactics were those of a naked savage, attacking from behind a fantastic screen of feathers and paint and a ferocious mask — a threat of danger when danger did not exist. . . .

Danaus had become a wanderer. He followed a northwesterly passage through inland meadows, avoiding the highways, stopping wherever there was food, roosting at night wherever he chanced to be. In a field of milkweed in southern New Hampshire, he found a virgin female who became his third mate, and when they parted, she flew north beyond the lakes and as far as Conway, laying her eggs along the way, but Danaus, flying northwest, came upon a part of the country laced with ponds and lakes and small rivers. He continued north until, in the vicinity of Danbury, he found among the rolling hills a hidden valley protected from the cold east winds — a bowl in which the heat of the days was trapped — a paradise of summer wild flowers. Owing to its unusual warmth, this isolated place was alive with all those small creatures which depend upon the heat of the sun to raise their body temperatures. It was an insect metropolis with a population numbering in the tens of thousands — a city with its inhabitants crowding all the available living space — a city of maximum mobility, incessant activity and continual predation, all of which were increased by a daily influx of foreign species — inhabitants of the woodland suburbs who came to the meadow to feed. In such an atmosphere, the arrival of Danaus made no difference, and he wove in and out among the flowers unnoticed and unchallenged. His identity soon merged with that of the field, the golden sheen of his wings melting into the universal patchwork of color and motion and sudden death.

In mid-afternoon of that day, the activity which had been at its height began unaccountably to abate, and a curious stillness settled over the field. Antiopa, the mourning cloak, who intermittently had been enjoying the sun of the field, now returned to his woodland habitat, and settling down on the trunk of an elm tree close under a large limb, closed his barklike wings, becoming invisible and small. Turnus, the great yellow swallowtail, flew deep into the woods and settled on a low branch in the same way, and Danaus, flying to the east side of an oak tree, crawled into a cluster of leaves, folded his wings so tightly that only one small triangle was exposed, and gripped the small meristem from which he hung with his four clawed feet. The motor sound of many bees and the click of locust wings fell away to silence until only the rusty squeak of one cricket scraped against the stillness. Nothing discernible had happened. No audible sound — no visible signal had warned of the approaching storm, but the insects knew. Perhaps it was the curious quality of static electricity in the air that gave them warning. Perhaps some subtle change in barometric pressures had set in motion an inaudible creeping telegraphy which passed from one insect to another, to another, making the meadow still.

Now a little smoky cloud began to gather in the west, rising and reaching out its fingers into the sky until it became a writhing mass of darkness growling with muted thunder, as though some flabby giant animal were preparing to pounce. It spread slate gray shadows over the trees and left on the horizon beneath it a cold pink fire. Pale flashes of lightning fanned out over the distant sky, and behind the blackness came wind and then rain. The rain spilled itself out in great clots, tearing at the leaves, stoning the flowers until they lay prostrate and bruised. It hurled itself against the trunks of trees and ran in streams down the cracks in the bark. Now it was that blades of lightning struck mercilessly into the meadow, into the wooded hillsides, slashing away the bark of trees, crashing into the high branches of the tall straight elm tree, which with a hoarse cry split from top to bottom and half of it fell sprawling onto the meadow so that antiopa, the mourning cloak, was instantly killed, but in the chaos he dropped into the drenched meadow unnoticed, as if he had never had life, but was only another fragment of bark. The air shook in the valley as thunder rebounded among the hills in long, terrifying, rhythmic groans, and water poured in a deluge onto the dirt road, filled the ruts and gutters with rivers of thin coffee-colored mud, and made of the meadow floor a swamp in which hundreds of the smallest insects struggled and drowned. Danaus, clinging to his oak stem, was flung wildly back and forth, shaken and buffeted until his wings were sodden and the minute hairs of his body were plastered against his abdomen, but he held fast to his perch all during the storm, the leaves protecting him from the full impact of the rain.

Nearly every aspect of the life of Danaus was governed, or at least affected, by the weather. As a newly hatched larva, he could drown in a droplet of water. He could not pupate successfully if the weather became too cold. In his chrysalis, the length of time required to complete the transformation from larva to butterfly was determined by the temperature, the amount of light, or a combination of these and other elements. At the end of June when the days were long and the weather hot and sunny, this change could take place in eight days. In September when the days were shorter and nights cooler, it might require three weeks. When the change was becoming complete and he was nearly dry and perfect in his shell, he knew in some mysterious way whether or not the weather was fair, and if it was not, he would delay his final development for an extra day rather than risk damage to his wings when they were still limp and tender by emerging in the rain.

Now after the storm had subsided, he hung quietly, still clinging to the stem of oak leaves, and waited for the water to evaporate from his wings so that he could fly. He hung motionless all night until the sun showed itself again the following morning and then he flew into the devastated field and perched on the trunk of the fallen tree. Gradually the insects which had survived the storm reappeared. The small butterflies which had hidden in the grasses had fared the worst, and such as remained of them were mostly ragged and pale. The meadow spider set about repairing the ruins of his elaborate silken screen, and the bees began to return unharmed from the distant hive where they had been safely sheltered.

Danaus perched in the sun sucking up moisture from the bark of the tree and slowly fanning his wings. They were still intact — nothing had been broken or torn, but the clear and luminous beauty of the day before was gone. The scales which gave them their color — each one as small as a grain of powder — had been dulled and flattened, and many had been rubbed off by the leaves of the tree and the wind. He seemed like a flower which is just beginning to fade. When the heaviness had left his wings, he flew again north, and eventually he crossed the Connecticut River into Vermont. He flew along the banks of the river, making short sorties into the adjoining countryside, and finally he came to a hillside which the migrating butterflies had found, and where some had stayed and bred. It had been mowed once, and from the old roots of the milkweed new shoots had sprung up which were a foot high when he arrived on the fifteenth of July. Here it was that he mated for the last time. He descended like a fireball upon an unsuspecting female, with a curious haste and violence unknown to him before. There was a brief rattling of wings in conflict, and an instant later he rose in the air clutching her in copulation.

It was here also that the last generation of eggs was laid. Most of the birds had finished feeding their young and gone elsewhere, and the field, undisturbed by man or beast, was in possession of the Monarchs. By August eighth, over two hundred larvae in this field were preparing to pupate, and by August twentieth most of these had emerged.

Further north in Maine where the first mate of Danaus had ended her journey, there were several fields, and the larvae here also numbered in the hundreds. The same was true of all the places where milkweed grew in abundance, for this was a summer when every change of weather had chanced to fall in a manner altogether favorable to the Monarchs. In addition to this, there had been favorable conditions the preceding winter so that more butterflies than usual had survived the cold season to fly north. Finally, the August days were exceptionally warm. Ordinarily, the last generation requires a much longer time to reach adult life than the early summer butterflies. If there is much rain or cold, the time between the egg and the butterfly can stretch to nearly two months, and then many emerge whose wings are deformed or who are too weak to fly. But this year throughout northern New England and as far west as the shores of Lake Ontario, thousands of newly emerged insects, which in other years might never have flown at all, would be ready to begin the long journey south before the first of September.

X

Midway
(July 15–22)

Yet each man kills the thing he loves,
By each let this be heard . . .

OSCAR WILDE

By the third week in July a midsummer lull had settled over the Meadow. The warblers had long since moved away, and the redwings, having reared two broods, had disappeared. The frantic commands of animals in the throes of teaching their young the necessity of being cautious had subsided. The first generation of black swallowtails had flown, laid their eggs and vanished, and the second generation had not yet emerged. The offspring of Danaus and his mate — those which had survived — were midway in their long green sleep. Topping their long hairy stems were the red plush tam o'shanters of devil's paintbrush, which flowered so brazenly while rooted in the ground and wilted so quickly and so timidly when picked. The

Queen Anne's lace was spreading its delicate bridal caps on one hand and offering its little green bird's nests on the other, and the milkweed's last drooping blossoms were tumbling over the tiny green pods which had just begun to form. Clusters of black-eyed Susans were in full bloom in the less dense grasses, and a large patch of tansy had spread until it was inextricably snarled in the thorns of the wild raspberries, which, when the wind blew, tore its leaves and filled the air with the scent of its seductive poison.

The three remaining larvae of acraea, the salt-marsh moth, having devastated the milkweed clump where they were born and exchanged their coats of soft gray fur for bristling dark brown ones, had finally attained a length of two and a half inches. They crawled away from their home plants to spin their cocoons, making their way through the grass with incredible speed. The first found part of an old crate and across the only remaining corner of it wove a shroud of his own silk, and his own woolly bristles which he rubbed from his skin. The second chose a large crack in the bark of an old oak tree, and the third, who had crawled onto the path, continued his journey until he reached the stone wall where he crept into a dry place between two stones to do his weaving. All three lay denuded of their brown fur and snug under their woven blankets. There in the darkness they modestly cast off their shaven skins and lay corn yellow and slippery until they had hardened into oval brown pupae.

The red milkweed beetle, like a slovenly housewife, had

taken leave of the disgusting mess for which she was responsible. She had flown briefly and, descending into the
grass, deposited her eggs at the base of a cleaner stalk of
milkweed. The eggs had hatched, and the larvae had bored
their way into the roots of the plant where they would eat
and sleep until the following spring.

The path through the Meadow was beginning to become
unnavigable. A waist-high forest of grasses and leafage
almost met across the middle of it, and out of the hard
crust of its surface sprang all those rankest of weeds which
habitually accept as their .share of the world the places
where nothing else will grow. In doing so, they are somehow rewarded with the choicest of blossoms — although
few take the trouble to look at them. In spring it had been
the yellow hop clover with its crisp shiny blooms which
had fastened its roots in the sand. Now each morning the
angular limbs of chicory, so ugly and so awkward in shape,
so harsh in texture, opened the most delicate of petals in
clear blue wheels, chiffon-thin and sky-colored. Long
racemes of butter and eggs, springing from scrawny stalks
in the barren ground, issued a subtle invitation to the bees,
and the rabbit-foot in soft fur buttons, bloomed gray-pink
among the stones.

Mr. Stevens arrived at the Meadow early Saturday morning to begin the annual task of clearing the way for his
jeep. He had meant to come the week before, but that had
been the night his sister and her whole family had arrived
to spend the night on their way to Maine. His house was

certainly a convenient stopping off place for them, and he
had enjoyed seeing them, but it wasn't the way it used to
be five years ago when — well, it wasn't the kind of a situation a man could deal with all alone, and he didn't believe
they had really enjoyed it. . . . He took his scythe from its
nail in the back room of his cabin and carried it over his
shoulder to the Meadow. This was work he liked to do.
He enjoyed the clear sound of the blade as it cut easily
through everything in its path, and he liked the rhythmic
motion of swinging it back and forth, which put life into
all his muscles. It gave him a sense of satisfaction to see the
ground he had cleared with the work of his hands — an
appreciation of man's true position in relation to the world
around him — that he could never feel when a machine was
doing the work for him. Man in his modern world was
dependent upon an endless chain of unnatural functions,
none of which must be allowed to break down or else his
whole structure would collapse. Power supply to commu-
nication to transportation to food distribution — everything would crumble and he would be alone with his own
ingenuity with no one to plow his drive, deliver his cord of
wood, or sell him shaving cream, and since the links in the
system could not reproduce themselves again, nature would
take over, and the grass would grow in great tufts through
the cracks in the cement, and the starlings would roost and
thrive in all the empty stores — along with the cock-
roaches, which, according to the scientists, would finally
have the last laugh. . . . So he stood in the sun and worked,
aware of the sound of an occasional cricket, and of the

sibilant message which his scythe kept repeating to him.
He stopped occasionally to look back at the clean swath
behind him, and he watched the stalks ahead as they fell
against each other in neat little parallel heaps. And as he
watched, his eyes chanced to fall on a thing that shone, and
on one of the fallen stalks he saw a second Chinese ear drop
— an exact duplicate of the one he had seen a month or
more before.

He laid down the scythe by the edge of the path and
picked up the fallen stem with its mystifying ornament,
which so surprised him by being there that he almost
thought it must be part of the plant. He examined the
other stalks close at hand to see if there might be a similar
drop suspended from each one. Discovering almost immediately that this was not the case, he set it aside, and when
he had finished his mowing for the day, took it back to the
cabin and stood it in an empty bottle.

He sat contemplating it as he relaxed with a cold drink
at the end of the day, thinking about how many marvels
were hidden in his little plot of land, and how many more
there must be if he only knew how to discover them. He
wanted them never to be destroyed — never to be disturbed. But lately whenever he thought about it, it was
with a feeling of helplessness. It was as if his thoughts were
accompanied by the muffled sound of a bulldozer which
was waiting in the distance to step in and take over as soon
as he was out of the way — unless he did something to
prevent it. But what could he do? Perhaps he could leave
the Meadow to the town to be used as a park. . . . But they

would never leave it the way it was. They would make it into *something*. There would be tennis courts, or sand boxes, swings, a public swimming pool. Nothing wrong with all these things, but that wasn't the point . . .

Even if they did leave it as it was, who would take care of it? Pretty soon people would begin to drive into it with their beer cans and their picnic papers — their hatchets and matches. And the raspberry vines, the fox's den — the blackbird's nest — the wild flowers. . . . No! He would leave it to the conservation people, cabin and all, and it would be a nature center. . . . But it was such a little piece of land. If only he had a hundred acres, or two hundred — but a little meadow like this, and this little woods? . . . At first, the whole idea had seemed so sensible and so comforting, but it wasn't comforting any more. What could a man do? How could you make people just leave something alone? What did they *ever* leave alone these days? Nothing but cemeteries — graveyards. No one was allowed to disturb a graveyard no matter how long it had been there — no matter how unkempt it was! A graveyard! What an irony! Well, why not? What was wrong with being buried in the middle of a big field with these wild flowers all around you. They wouldn't save his Meadow just to preserve all these fascinating kinds of life, but they would *have* to save it in order not to disturb the sleep of the dead! What a ghoulish thought! But it struck him as being so ridiculous that he laughed aloud, which broke the gloom and then he felt better.

The chrysalis which Mr. Stevens had propped up in an

empty bottle was one of the offspring of Danaus and his first mate, and there were twenty others sprinkled throughout the Meadow. In a week's time, all had emerged and gone their separate ways with the exception of one which fell before its wings were dry and, lying helpless and soft in the grass, was consumed by the toad who had the good fortune to be making his way through the undergrowth to the path at just that moment.

Of the remaining nineteen, nine were females and ten were males. They emerged a few at a time for four days, and some of the first were still in the Meadow when the last one made his appearance. There were other Monarchs belonging to other parents, to other generations, to other fields, for by now the migrating butterflies, their children and their children's children had all moved northward. All had intermingled into one great population, and the specific genealogy of any individual could no longer be determined. The heritage of each was the heritage of all the rest, for each belonged to the great genetic pool which reached from Florida to Ontario — from the Appalachian range to the entire eastern seaboard.

By now the summer solstice had long passed, and from each twenty-four hours a few minutes of sunlight were being whittled away; perhaps only two minutes each day, and yet these two minutes — a tiny thread in the all-encompassing fabric of the weather — had already begun to weave their spell over the lives of the butterflies. The impulse to move north was abating, and while some started northward in a rather undecided manner, others were content to remain close to the place where they had been born. Some of the offspring of Danaus mated, laid their first eggs in the Meadow and continued the voyage north. Some mated but were unable to reproduce, and others did not mate at all. Those females which did not reproduce would live to join the great southern migration, while those who laid their eggs would die. But *their* offspring — the third generation to be born in the Meadow — the great grand-children of Danaus the mother — would produce no young. Some would indulge in futile copulation, but no eggs would develop in the ovarioles of the females, and the males would be unable to deliver sperm sacs to the females.

The members of the sub-order Rhopalocera — the but-terflies — in order to keep their various species alive, have developed devices enabling them to counteract the rigors of winter, to remain dormant during the months when their larval food plants are also dormant. Each species has solved these problems in its own way, according to the inscrutable rules governing the process of evolution. The first genera-tions, born during the spring and early summer, live with happy abandon, making no provision for the problems which they will never live to face, but to the last generation falls the responsibility of perpetuating its species. They do not all abide by the same rules, but each one grapples with the paralyzing hand of winter according to the rules set down by his own species, and not by the rules of any other species. The last mourning cloak, emerging in August or September, goes into hibernation without mating, and whatever the shelter he has chosen, whether a cellarway, a crevice under the bark of a hollow tree, a dark corner beneath the eaves of a barn — he remains there nearly motionless, turning only a few degrees perhaps twice during the winter. Thus he hibernates until the first warm sun breaks the cold grip of February, and he mates only when the willow leaves are green slivers on the twig. The swallowtails — polyxenes in the northeast, or philenor of the steel blue hindwings in the south, or ajax of the middle west with his sword-like tails, his zebra stripes above, his blood red gashes below, or turnus, the tiger, whose black, streaked, butter yellow wings often measure seven inches across — all of the swallowtails, whatever their tribe, pass the winter as chrysalids. The larvae, after excreting the last fluids and wastes within their bodies, attach themselves to some dark indefinite colored surface — be it vertical, horizontal, or diagonal, it makes no difference. There they pupate, and sleep out the winter looking like little inch-long swaddled teddy bears. Archippus, the viceroy, when only halfway through his larval life, sews the petiole of his leaf to its stem with silken thread so that it cannot fall, rolls the leaf around himself, and under a coverlet of silk, sleeps until the new leaves are big enough to finish nourishing him the following spring. The Monarch does none of these things, but turns again south, and choosing a place warm enough so that his body fluids will not crystalize, yet cold enough to slacken his rate of metabolism, passes the winter months in partial consciousness, waiting for his reproductive organs to mature and for the milkweed to sprout once more.

A butterfly emerged from the chrysalis that Mr. Stevens had left in his cabin, and in due time made its first flight. When Mr. Stevens returned at the end of a week, he found it hopelessly entangled in a spider web which had been spun across the corner of his sunniest window. The spider, intimidated by the enormous size of his captive, had withdrawn, but the butterfly, although it had destroyed the web in its struggle to escape, had perished. It was still limp when Mr. Stevens released it from its death-trap, and he spread it on the table to look at it — the crown of its palpi, its wings, a mantle of cloth of gold, and the erect, almost haughty way its head was held — somehow regal, even in death. It was then that he noticed the now withered piece of milkweed which he had left in the empty bottle, and the empty shell hanging from it — like a little glass slipper; the slipper and the prince — but where was Cinderella? With this he began to recall little wisps of faraway happenings — little jig-saw fragments of his boyhood — a caterpillar he had once held captive in a jar, a field on the way home from school where he had tried to catch butterflies in his cap — a nature walk his fourth grade teacher had taken them on and he had been punished for chewing gum — fragments of stories . . . a little girl peering over a tremendous mushroom . . . "but when you have to turn into a chrysalis — you will someday, you know — and then, after that, into a butterfly —" and suddenly everything fell into place — the striped caterpillar, the chrysalis, and the butterfly. It was all there. It had been there all the time, and he had been too blind to see it!

He felt the surge of satisfaction that comes with learning some absolutely new thing, and he felt compelled to test his world in the light of his new knowledge. He went out into his Meadow and waded through the grass with long strides, the grasshoppers jumping out of his path like popcorn, and the pollen on the flowers brushing off on his clothes. He saw the Monarchs flying back and forth, feeding, dropping out of sight into the field and making themselves invisible, and he had a new sense of oneness with everything around him. He was part of the Meadow. He had learned the secrets of the animals and the birds, and now he would learn the secrets of the insects as well. He knew the fox better than the fox knew him, and now he could share with the fox the privilege of being lord of the Meadow.

XI

Interlude

(July 15–August 21)

When fishes flew and forests walked,
  And figs grew upon thorn
Some moment when the moon was blood,
  Then surely I was born;

                    G. K. Chesterton

*The life cycles of Danaus (above)
and of archippus the viceroy (below*

WHILE DANAUS was at the hillside field in Vermont, he sometimes roosted at night in a black willow tree by a brook at the bottom of the field. It was a large tree — so large that Danaus himself was unaware that the age-old drama in which he himself had so recently taken part was being enacted again among its branches. This time it was

archippus the viceroy who was laying her eggs, and since her offspring were able to survive on a variety of trees, she had flown about the countryside depositing one egg here, one there, on the leaf tip of an aspen, a poplar, and had finally found the willow tree.

She belonged to the family of the Nymphalidae, a family closely related to the Danaids. Her front legs, like those of Danaus, were held folded. She laid only one egg on each tree so that each one, when it hatched, must, like Danaus, make its way in the world alone.

There would be the same interplay of life and death — parasites and predators, the same desperate struggle for survival — the same search for protection by some sort of trompe l'oeil, the same loss of life — the same triumph of the strongest few. And this time the drama would end in a riddle.

Her eggs were squat and covered with a moldlike fuzz. In a few short days they hatched, and one of them was on the willow tree scarcely a foot from the spot where Danaus had roosted the night before. It was one of the ugliest of all larvae. At first, it was dark brown and oily, streaked with pasty white — a nearly perfect imitation of a bird dropping. It rested immobile during most of the day and fed at night when none could watch it. When it molted, like Danaus, it ate its discarded skin, and it continued to look like a bird dropping, especially when it lay stretched along a leaf, or when it lay limply with its head drooping down from the twig to which it had fastened itself. With each molt a new series of spiny growths, drab in color, irregular in form, burgeoned from its new skin. At times it drew its head in out of sight beneath it and wound itself around the twig so crookedly that it took on the appearance of a fungus growth or a mold or a scale or some other unappetizing thing. It behaved as though it were either afraid or ashamed to be alive. It even seemed to withdraw from the pleasant task of eating, for it consumed in all not more than fifteen leaves of the willow tree.

Full grown, instead of being glossy and smooth as the handsome caterpillar of Danaus had been, it was a mass of branching spines, grotesque, awkward, and, as a caterpillar, quite unrecognizable.

It spun a silken foothold into which it secured its anal prolegs as Danaus had done and hung head down. When it finally pupated, the chrysalis of archippus, in sharp contrast to the glistening smooth, jewellike chrysalis of Danaus, was blotched in greasy brown and chalk gray, and a large wart-like growth had sprouted from its dorsal side. It hung as crookedly from its twig as the dead willow leaf beside it which was brown and gray and curling.

The chrysalis of Danaus had hung in motionless repose. That of archippus was not only able to distort itself at will, but to remain in a warped position indefinitely, brown and gray and twisted beside the dead willow leaf.

In two weeks archippus the viceroy pushed his way out of this unsightly mummy case, clung to it while his wings expanded, and in six minutes he had miraculously become an almost perfect image of Danaus. His wings contained the same glowing fire, had the same black-veined scales, and were bordered by the same black and white lace. Even his body bore the same fine black and white hairs. It was a startling likeness.

Not for a moment in the entire course of his life until now had archippus borne the slightest resemblance to Danaus, and yet somehow in the dark of his chrysalis — in the secret confines of his genes — this had happened. Archippus emerged, and suddenly the two butterflies were so amazingly alike that one could hardly be distinguished from the other.

How had it all happened? Which butterfly had first worn this amulet, the Monarch or the viceroy? Which had followed suit? And, the digressions of nature being infinite in variety but none the less logical, to what end?

It is believed that the protection of the Monarch came first, and that over the ages the viceroy has grown to resemble him, thereby gaining a selective advantage — a quality which in some way enables him to avoid destruction by his natural predators. The particular wing pattern which now protects the viceroy must first have worked to protect the Monarch, but how? The Monarch larva feeds upon milkweed, which to some other creatures is slightly poisonous. It is reasoned that since the larva feeds upon milkweed, the resulting Monarch butterfly must be distasteful or repugnant — so repugnant that a bird, having tasted an undetermined number of Monarchs would at length remember the experience with unerring clarity. He would remember not only the taste but the colors — the very geometric design of the wings of the butterfly, and having once learned, would never again eat a butterfly of the same appearance. This being the case, the palatable viceroy would also be spared by looking like the Monarch. . . .

But the factors which must necessarily have interlocked for such a mimicry of one insect by another to develop, make it the most amazing and the most tenuous of all protective devices. Protective coloration is a widespread and indispensable adjunct to survival. Myriads of insects and other animals melt into their surroundings, invisible in an aura of centuries-old camouflage — the striped chipmunk, the bark-colored squirrel, the stick caterpillars, the night hawk warming her pebble-like eggs on a barren rock, and the young fawn, alert and frozen against the pine needles and shimmering spring green of the forest floor. The butterfly, antiopa, the mourning cloak, is thus protected by resting with closed wings on the bark of the willow tree for long hours at a time. But antiopa is one of the most lethargic of butterflies. He has earned his camouflage by remaining still and waiting for the slow wheels of evolution by natural selection to provide it. It happened in the beginning that if the wings of the butterfly resembled the tree, the birds did not see it, and it was spared. Mourning cloaks whose wings were too light or too bright were discovered and eaten. Those which survived mated, passing along in their genes the deceptive coloring of the tree, so that an ever greater number of their descendants became protected from the birds which could no longer find them.

In this way all animal camouflage is the result of a specialized kind of "survival of the fittest" in which fitness can be defined as some slight but advantageous mutation in the genes responsible for pigmentation. Such camouflage develops most readily when a species which is not too peripatetic receives protection from a stationary species, as does the butterfly antiopa, resting on the bark of a tree, or the chrysalis of the viceroy which emulates the willow leaf hanging beside it on the same stem.

But it is an infinitely more remarkable adaptation for the viceroy, which has become a butterfly, to gain protection by resembling another flying insect. Not only the genetic heritage of one butterfly is involved here, but the genetic heritage of two butterflies. In all probability neither the Monarch nor the viceroy has come unchanged from its beginnings to the present day, and if one has been protected by resembling the other, the evolution of the shape and color of both their wings must have been parallel. The process has been further complicated by the fact that Monarch butterflies migrate over an enormous area, forming hundreds — even thousands — of transient populations. Casually observed, all Monarchs look alike, but in distantly separated areas, in different climates, at different seasons, individuals in these populations sometimes show startling variations in size and color. Originally the viceroy's protection grew from a selective process by which only those individuals most like the Monarch were spared. His safety now rests with the discrimination of the predatory birds in attacking the aberrant Monarchs which sometimes look less like Monarchs than viceroys do. A continuation of the typical Monarch form, which the viceroy more nearly resembles, is thus assured.

The mimicking viceroy is further faced with problems of numbers, of timing, and of food supply. If the Monarchs are to protect the viceroys successfully, there must already be Monarchs flying whenever and wherever the viceroys emerge — Monarchs enough for the viceroys to become lost among them. This is because the bird must eat a Monarch before eating a viceroy if he is to associate an unpleasant taste with this particular wing pattern. If there were more viceroys than Monarchs, a bird might, by the laws of chance, eat many viceroys before tasting his first Monarch, and the confusion thus created in his mind might take a lifetime of trial and error to resolve. Clearly, under these conditions neither insect would be efficiently protected.

Therefore a viceroy could not gain adequate protection simply by being in the path of the Monarch's spring migration, when the Monarchs are flying singly and do not remain in one place for long. Only in the breeding grounds could there be enough Monarchs for a long enough time and in sufficient numbers to afford security. But the breeding grounds are determined by the abundance of milkweed, which is the food of the Monarch larvae, but not of the viceroy. Close to each Monarch breeding ground, then, there must be at least one willow or other suitable tree for the young of the viceroy to feed upon — and this must have been so throughout history, unless the viceroy has been versatile enough in his adaptations to alter completely his feeding requirements.

It must also be that, to assure their protection, the over-wintering viceroy larvae in these trees must either emerge, mate and lay their eggs before the marauding birds arrive to eat them, or else remain hidden in the safety of their chrysalids until after the first generation of Monarchs has emerged. In how many places, with what delicate timing and rhythmic frequency, must so many diverse conditions all have been brought together to insure a nearly perfect protection by mimicry for the viceroy!

There are other fascinating ramifications to the problem of mimicry which are still unexplained. For instance, all of the foregoing events do not take into account that from year to year there is a drastic and seemingly unreasonable fluctuation in numbers of Monarchs. How does the viceroy find protection during the years when almost no Monarchs are to be seen?

Then there are the various faculties of the predatory bird. He was tricked into *not* seeing the larva and the chrysalid — a natural oversight. He can see the butterfly, and he must decide, after one or two trials, whether to eat it or not on the basis of sight alone. In addition to his sight and his judgment, his sense of taste is also involved. Who knows just how distasteful a Monarch really is to any given species of bird?

Some Danaids have been found with beak marks on their wings, leading to the theory that birds have nipped their wings, tasted them, and allowed them to escape. This suggests that even the dry wings, which contain no bodily fluids, and their covering of powdery scales were distasteful to some particular bird. Under certain experimental conditions birds have been observed eating Monarchs as readily as any other available food, and under other conditions, other birds will not eat them at all.

What is the criterion by which any bird separates a good taste from a bad taste? Presuming that he is able to do so, his memory must also come under scrutiny. How long is a bird capable of remembering? Some experiments have shown that in captivity some wild birds can remember a learned lesson for as long as two and a half weeks. Left in natural circumstances could they still remember? Can they remember from year to year, or must a Monarch be sacrificed to each bird each year in order that the bitter lesson may be relearned? And what exactly is the bitter lesson? If the Monarch really is repulsive to taste, is it the milkweed that makes it so, or is the taste caused by some digestive juice which would be bitter to the same bird's tongue regardless of what the butterfly had eaten? Perhaps the villain is neither the milkweed nor a digestive juice, but some ill-smelling glandular secretion, exuded under stress and not detectable by man.

Some experiments indicate that under natural conditions healthy new butterflies, especially colorful ones, whether they are considered tasteful or distasteful, are not a major staple of the ornithic diet, possibly because they are too large and formidable, too swift and erratic in flight to warrant pursuit. Perhaps among butterflies it is only the old, the slow, the injured and the weak which regularly fall prey to the birds.

Any living creature, in whatever guise, has evolved to the present day because his appearance affords him some protection. Otherwise, he would not have survived. And so there is the Monarch and there is the viceroy. That they should be almost "identical twins" despite their genetic differences, their diverse physical requirements, their unique and particular habits, seems as much a mystery as a proof of mimicry. The ultimate secret behind their resemblance has not yet been disclosed — the final word not spoken.

By the edge of the brook there was a dead squirrel, and archippus the viceroy alighted upon it (because all viceroys have a penchant for carrion). Danaus saw him there and at first took him for one of his own kind. He fluttered over him, expecting to mate, but although he had been deceived by the wings of archippus, something — perhaps some unfamiliar motion or some unusual scent — told him that he was mistaken, and he flew away. . . . Archippus mated later on, and some of the eggs he fertilized were laid on the same willow tree. When the little larvae were less than half an inch long, each one rolled himself into a willow leaf, stitched the edges of it together with silk, and settled down to a long winter's sleep. They would wait until spring to accomplish the longest part of their transformation. Then, abetted by the right combination of wind, warmth and weather, they might complete their work before the arrival of the birds.

XII

Journey's End
(August 21–September 10)

Further in summer than the birds,
Pathetic from the grass
A minor nation celebrates
Its unobtrusive mass.

EMILY DICKINSON

IT WAS the third week in August. In the Meadow there was now none of the excitement of procreation. The goldenrod had begun to bloom, and there were ripe blackberries. The tips of the fireweed were still magenta flames, but lower down on the stems the long needlelike seed pods had burst like miniature rockets at the touch of the goldfinch's beak, and in bursting had loosed their clouds of downy smoke which clung to the drying leaves of the plant until a puff of wind should carry them away.

The three acraea moths had finally emerged. When last seen as caterpillars they had been over two and a half inches long and were wearing bulging black lacquered caps and coats of stiff brown fur. They reappeared as moths only one inch long clothed in snowy white and buttercup yellow with a peppering of black on their wings. The one female

among them lay for only an hour against the bark of the tree where she had emerged from her cocoon before the males found her.

The blossoms of the milkweed had dried and fallen to the ground while the leaves had become darkened and coarse. No Monarchs were there to settle on them because the children of Danaus had flown away, and the two grand-children of Danaus which had thus far survived had formed their chrysalids and would not emerge for another week. Then they, too, would fly away. A time of lethargy had begun. The air of the Meadow was no longer fresh with the smell of new leaves nor heavy with the delicious per-fume of clover and milkweed, but permeated with the pollen of goldenrod and the strong sweet fragrance of hay. The change of the smell of things was a subtle change, and in Mr. Stevens, returning from a three weeks' vacation, it aroused a vague feeling of apprehension — of having for-gotten something important.

The cabin, too, seemed to have lost some indefinable measure of its snug security. The summer home of his sister, whom he had been visiting, had been endlessly alive with the clamor of children, and now the solitude of his own little log house was being broken by remembered sounds — echoes of bare feet running, and of voices laugh-ing as they called him to come and look! He had spent long hours with his ten-year-old niece, Ragna, a child whose enthusiasm and intelligence and natural grace de-lighted him as much as her elfin face and untamed chestnut hair amused him. They had roamed the fields and ponds and shores together. They had swapped yarns about their wild friends and they had gone on frogging and snaking expeditions and turtle hunts. They had gone butterflying and clamming. There had been a wonderful moment early one evening when they had gone star gazing and a delicate-footed young deer had been outlined among the trees in the apple orchard.

As he stood in the Meadow late in August searching for the cause of his uneasiness, Mr. Stevens began to sense that he, as well as the Meadow, had somehow changed, but that in changing, he and the Meadow had moved apart. In the Meadow everything seemed to be approaching an end, but in him it seemed that a kind of excitement was just beginning to awaken.

For nearly five years he had cherished the times when he could be alone, and he had visited his family only at their insistence. But this last time, a weekend with them had stretched into a week — into three weeks. Now he found himself missing their gaiety and thinking about Ragna scrambling over the rocks in her cut-off dungarees, when he should have been alert for the thin squeak of a chipmunk or the first triangle of migrating geese. This disruption of his harmonious rapport with the Meadow was confusing, and he did not realize that the thing he had forgotten was sorrow. He was not aware that for the first time since his wife had died, he really wanted companionship. . . .

Sometime during the third week of August, the tide began to turn. The heat of the days had not yet subsided, but the nights had already become cooler, and with fewer hours of warmth and sunlight, the activity of the insects had also lessened. As the headwaters of a tidal river slacken and grow still, so had the Monarchs, at the limits of their migration, halted their northern course. And, as the still waters commence to turn and tremble at the flood, so did the butterflies begin to turn back, ebbing slowly out of their northern breeding grounds. The territories where the Monarchs had gathered became a series of enormous slowly forming whirlpools from which tiny rivulets of butterflies were slowly drained away.

Danaus was not aware of the gentle turbulence which had begun. He was only aware that one day he was compelled to leave the hillside in Vermont and start back in the direction from which he had come. There were others flying through the sultry August heat. The sun beat down on a shimmering countryside, undisturbed by any wind. High in the trees, the reedy drone of the cicadas rose and died away like a humming top. Although he was not aware of it, Danaus was following in the path of several other Monarchs, and when the shadows began to stretch out, they all settled for the night in the branches of an oak tree near the east bank of the Connecticut River. When it began to be dusk, the first cricket sounded his pitchpipe, and before long from the trees, from the grass, from the crevices in the stone walls, rose the sadness of late summer which is tempered with resignation. It rose in unison and in thin dissonances — in rhythm and in syncopation — in the texture of silk and the texture of sand, and it squeezed

the air with the poignancy of its throbbing. So the plain-
tive notes of the chickadee and the white-throated sparrow,
whistled in a minor key as they combed the dead flowers
for seeds. The sun dropped out of sight, and a black scarf
of starlings cast its shade briefly between one tree and
another.

About two weeks earlier, a handful of butterflies which
had bred in Ontario had started to drift south and east,
slowly making their way toward the ocean. Also, the first
of those which had bred on the island in Maine had crossed
south to the mainland one still, sunny day, and continued
south, following a crooked course which took them sometimes into sight of the ocean and sometimes into nearby
fields of late wild flowers.

By the time Danaus reached the coast the first of the
migrants from Ontario and Maine, and one or two from
Conway, New Hampshire, were also there; and together
they roosted, perhaps thirteen in all, on a tree near Hampton Beach in New Hampshire.

By now the wings of Danaus had grown thin and semi-
translucent. The storm in Danbury had robbed them of
their luster, but it had also weakened the tiny hinges which
held the minute powdery scales to his wing membranes,
and gradually they had been flaking away. His pointed
forewings had become feathered along their tips, and
because of these ragged edges, his flight was more labored,
and he was able to travel fewer miles in a day. Some of the
Monarchs flew on ahead of him, and others who had started

later joined him, so that each night he roosted with a new group. After several days he reached Plum Island, just south of Newburyport in Massachusetts.

This island is a long spit of land running parallel to the coastline, and separated from it by salt marshes and a network of tidal rivers. The island is composed largely of sand dunes, out of which grow beach grass and ground lupine and very little else. It extends along the coast for a distance of about five miles. At the northern end there is a summer colony of many small cottages packed closely together on the sand, each having its own individual style of architecture — or lack of it — some bearing name plates like "Drift In," "Sand Box," and "Surf Border." The eaves of some are underscored with wooden scrollwork, and others boast porches supported by spindly Doric columns. There is an occasional willow or poplar tree, planted in the hope of coaxing a little shade onto a roof here and there, and an assortment of overturned rowboats are sandwiched between cottages, leaving hardly enough room for a child to squeeze past them.

The gaiety of summer was now but an echo, coming from the blackened windows, from trash barrels and cartons of beer cans by the roadside and from the boarded up Dairi-Freez and hot dog stands at the end of the causeway leading to the island from the mainland. The deserted colony looked somehow unloved and unkempt. Cottages which had been freshly painted a few months before now showed the ravages of the broiling summer sun, the wind, sand, and rain. Drifts of fine sand had piled up on the porches of the front line of cottages. Many were stained with rust caused by cheap screens or by the defective kind of plumbing usually found in summer cottages of like age. The effect was somehow reminiscent of a caravan of camels huddled together in the desert before a sand storm.

It was into this desolate setting that the Monarchs descended. There were sixteen of them, and they arrived one at a time, each about five minutes after the one before. They found neither food nor shelter in the vicinity of the cottages and continued along the dunes, flying back and forth looking for nectar, but a few struggling spears of seaside goldenrod were all that they could find. On the east, the sea pounded without cease, gouging away the sand a little more each year, and undercutting the dunes, while at the same time the wind built them up, until by now the breaking waves could only be heard from the cottages, and not seen at all.

The southern part of the island was a wildlife sanctuary — a stopping place for a great variety of sea birds, and the air was filled with their cries. The sand seemed to go endlessly on, disappearing in the mists created by the surf. There were scarcely any trees, but there were occasional beach plum bushes, and at the far end of the reservation, the Monarchs found one of these upon which they alighted at about four o'clock in the afternoon, clinging to a branch on the southeast side of it. When darkness fell, it was the silken darkness of a moonless night untroubled by street lights or the headlights of automobiles, or by any sound except the pounding of the sea. The horizon was still

washed with a border of faint salmon pink, when out of the
sky came the pale gold disc of a single first water star. It
sent its long thin thread of light across the blue veil of the
ocean to the island, and Danaus, hanging motionless on the
beach plum bush, perceived a dim blur of distant light,
which was the star repeated more than fifty thousand times
in his marvelous insect eyes. . . .

In the morning there was a light breeze from the north,
and by nine o'clock the warm sun had encouraged the
butterflies to leave their branch. They flew among the
dunes for a while, but they were still unable to find nourishment, and before long the first of the sixteen headed south
across the mouth of the little bay separating Plum Island
from Crane's Beach. The second followed in his wake a

few minutes later, and so on for an hour and a half or more, when Danaus was the last to leave. The thin procession made its way from the southern tip of Plum Island to Crane's Beach, a broad and beautiful expanse of white sand and dunes and sparkling waters — and from Crane's Beach to Annisquam, and from Annisquam to Eastern Point in Gloucester, which juts out into the sea, presenting a long front to the open ocean on the east and another long front to a small bay on its west side.

Over the years the breakers and the wind had gradually pushed the shoreline into a barrier extending the whole length of the eastern side, which gave the center of the little peninsula the appearance of being below sea level — especially since a large portion of it was a brackish marsh criss-crossed with drainage channels which were more or less concealed by a tangled undergrowth of poison ivy, wild blueberry, and some cranberry. But over and above this tangle, the whole point was a mass of rushes and fall flowers. The grasses were waist high, but the flowers in many places were shoulder high. Cattails were crowded into the lowest and wettest areas, but most of the marsh was filled with goldenrod and fall asters just beginning to come into bloom. The marsh was protected from the wind by the height of the sand barrier, and with no trees to shade it, the sun beat down on it during the day, warming the wet ground and inhibiting the frost. The combination of moisture and heat produced not only an ideal situation for the flowers, which habitually bloomed until late in October, but a paradise for the migrating butterflies who could feed there undisturbed for as long as they wished before continuing south across the next body of water.

When Danaus arrived at this marsh at three o'clock in the afternoon, he found himself in the company of about twenty other Monarchs, all feeding and resting in the sun. Most were sparkling with newness, some were older, but none were as faded and as tattered as he. In another hour all of the company began to leave the marsh and fly around in the branches of the trees belonging to several small adjacent estates. It was now the seventh of September. The nights were becoming quite cool, especially near the ocean, and by half past four Danaus was roosting with the others, concealed by leaves, high in an oak tree.

When the sun rose the following morning, the sky was clear and as was their habit, the Monarchs left their tree as soon as the warm rays had penetrated their bodies. They returned to the marsh and flew among the flowers, feeding and enjoying the warm air. At about half past ten in the morning, one of them flew up and across the sand barrier — out over the water — but after a few moments it glided back into the marsh.

During the night the wind had changed and there was now a light southerly breeze coming in from the ocean. The Monarchs could easily fly against it, but to fly directly south from Eastern Point, it was necessary to cross a twenty-two-mile stretch of uninterrupted water. Over the land, a flight of this distance against the wind was easily accomplished, for the butterflies could always alight and rest. If blown to one side of their path or the other, or high

into the air by a stray gust, they could maneuver themselves onto a tree or tall shrub until able to continue once
more, but over water they had no choice other than to fly.
If forced to alight on the water against the wind, they
would risk being buffeted by both wind and wave, and in
order to rise from the surface of the sea, they would have
to fly with the wind, thus losing a large part of the distance
they had gained. Some obscure instinct warned them to
avoid this hazard, and so they tested the wind by making
short sorties over the sea, lifting their wings and gliding
back to the safety of land if the wind proved unfavorable.
From time to time during the day, others among the Monarchs tested the wind in this same way, not trying to fly
against it but merely ascertaining its direction. At about
half past two in the afternoon, Danaus flew up and across
the barrier of sand, but the wind slipped through the ragged
edges of his wings, marring his efficiency and slowing his
progress, and he was blown back before he even reached
the water's edge.

The following day two more Monarchs arrived and they
also fed, tested the wind, and roosted at night. By afternoon of the third day, there were twenty-six butterflies in
the marsh, and the wind was still from the south, blowing
a little stronger than before. By now most of the summer
butterflies had disappeared and were preparing to spend
the winter in some state of suspended animation — some
like archippus, the viceroy, as larvae, others like polyxenes,
the black swallowtail, as chrysalids, or antiopa, the mourning cloak, as butterflies. Some would even hibernate as

newly laid eggs. Only the last straggling butterflies of the last summer brood remained on the wing — two or three worn white cabbage butterflies fluttering like scraps of a rejected love letter — and a swallowtail, his black wings fragments of ash floating on the air.

On the third day, Danaus again flew up to test the wind. This time as he strove to surmount the sand barrier an unexpected updraft caught and lifted him, and with a sudden spurt of power he fought the air with his wings in response to it. He sailed up and over the open water — free, strong, a solitary spark of energy in the blue sky. Then, as suddenly as it had come, his energy ebbed away. His great wing muscles failed so that he could beat the air no more, and he was at the mercy of the wind which knows no mercy. It forced him to complete the loop he had begun, and flung him down against the crest of a wave which washed him onto the beach. He lay on his side, struggling to right himself, but his wings were glued together and plastered to the wet shore, and his flailing legs could not find a foothold in the sand. A second later, the undertow sucked him back again, dragging him across the sand and the stones, and a second wave crashed over him, crushing him between itself and the sibilating shore. A third wave caught him up, and flung him high on the beach in a shower of crystals. But Danaus was already dead. He lay in a pool of creamy foam, the little salty bubbles breaking around him in tiny whispered explosions; his faded wings nearly matching the paleness of the sand beneath him; the black veins of his wings mingling with the black strands of dead seaweed. He was camouflaged in death as he had rarely been in life.

The life of Danaus since the moment when he first emerged from his chrysalis had lasted for two months and seventeen days. His golden wings had carried him for over 400 miles, and 1700 eggs had been fertilized with his sperm. Only the strongest of his tribe could boast such accomplishments. Some of the spring males had mated only once and died. Some who were less alert or less aggressive than Danaus had lost their lives before mating at all.

Of the 1700 eggs, seventy-five had completed the cycle of change to become butterflies. The weak and the defective had perished, leaving only the most perfect to perpetuate a society based upon genetic competence.

Not all of the seventy-five would complete the southern migration, and of those who did, not all would survive the winter to mate in the spring. But even if only five of his offspring should survive and mate, it would be more than enough to assure continuance of the tribe of Danaus.

The great southern migration had begun. It had begun with a few scattered butterflies in a few scattered fields — so few that their presence was hardly noticed as they flew among the flowers — so few that even when they roosted together, they could not easily be seen. It started in the same way that a few leaves fall day by day for perhaps three weeks, and then suddenly the wind blows and in three days the trees are bare. It started in the same way that a few drops of rain leak from the edges of a cloud, and then after a time the black rain pours down engulfing the earth. The first twenty-six butterflies at Eastern Point had come without arousing any interest. By the time they finally departed, still unnoticed, four more had joined them, and so a total of thirty butterflies started on their way again when the wind finally changed on the fourth day and came out of the north. By half past seven in the morning, they had all begun the twenty-two-mile trip across the mouth of Boston Harbor from Eastern Point on the north shore to Strawberry Point on the south shore. With the help of the wind, the Monarchs could easily fly this distance in less than half a day, and from Strawberry Point there were at least thirty-five miles of land by any southerly route before another major water crossing was necessary. As the migration progressed, there would be greater and greater numbers of Monarchs — larger colonies roosting at night — and a variety of routes south, and one of these routes led across Mr. Stevens' Meadow.

XIII

The Tidal Wave

(September 17–October 19)

The wind blows out, the bubble dies
The spring entombed in autumn lies
The dew dries up, the star is shot
The flight is past — and man forgot.

HENRY KING

WHEN the thirty Monarchs left Eastern Point, their absence was not noticed because they had hardly departed when others began to arrive. The next day there were more, and the next still more. The numbers to be seen on the point at any time always depended on the direction of the wind.

By the seventeenth of September, great numbers of butterflies were approaching. All the way from the Canadian border they could be seen flying southeast and then following the coastline south. They could be seen in the fields, crossing the streets and highways, among the gardens, usually flying singly or in twos and threes — or flying high above the telephone poles, quickly and without swerving in their southern course. Small groups often mingled with each other, but when they flew directly and with urgency,

they flew not in masses as blackbirds fly, not in formation as geese fly, but in thin files, perhaps fifteen seconds or so apart.

On the nineteenth of September they filtered into the marsh at Eastern Point all day long. The seaside goldenrod and the asters were at the peak of their blooming — great frothy plumes of goldenrod and domes of New England asters encrusted with violet or magenta blossoms, each an inch in diameter — the scepter and the crown — a field of royal purple and royal gold stretching almost to the sea.

By nightfall there were over 200 Monarchs in the marsh, and the wind had changed once more. For three days longer it blew in from the south while the migrating Monarchs, converging along the coast from all their summer haunts, continued to arrive.

By the fourth day there were upwards of 3000 butterflies at Eastern Point. They flew along the streets, in gardens, gathered in droves on the delicious blossoms. It was impossible to say how many there were, for while many were flying, others were resting, and so the field seemed to be in continuous motion as their wings, like little flecks of fire, darted in every direction, rose and fell, appeared and vanished. Among them were children and grandchildren of Danaus and all of his four mates, and offspring of his brothers and their mates, and the brothers and sisters of his mates and their children, and of other butterflies from other places that Danaus and his tribe had never seen.

Each afternoon the pattern was the same. First a few butterflies soared into the treetops and came to rest, and as the others flew close, those which had already settled flashed open their wings, just as Danaus had done when the phoebe had passed behind him on his first day, and later when his safety had been threatened by polyxenes. But here in the treetops, perhaps the same gesture did not signify a warning, but an invitation. Perhaps it contained the elements of both, for although each night hundreds of Monarchs roosted together on the same branch, they did not disturb each other.

As the numbers continued to increase, the butterflies became less wary. All summer long, when a single Monarch had been flying alone, he had been alert and ready to flee if he sensed motion less than ten feet away. Now, when there were others of his kind all around him — when two dozen or more were maneuvering for space on a single clump of flowers — he showed no caution at all. A woman appeared with a camera and waded through the marsh, oblivious of the canals and the poison ivy. She stood within arm's length, sidling, stooping, leaning, indulging in all facets of the ritual of picture-making — the gestures and motions, the repeated trials and errors and triumphs, and the Monarchs came and went as if she did not exist. A man who was working in his garden nearby stood in the midst of them and they flew all around his head, alighting on the very flowers he was trimming. They seemed to be basking in sunlight and security.

But safety is never certain and, like a false lover, it betrays those who lower the barriers of caution in its presence. As the Monarchs glided lazily through the trees, a young kingbird sat motionless on a gray branch, waiting. And when his moment came, he darted out and snatched his prey from the air, gobbling its body while its burnished wings fluttered to the ground. But the cuckoo plunged down recklessly upon its prey, and crushing the Monarch with its beak, devoured it wings and all.

Why had the butterflies suddenly grown so inured to the possibility of danger? It almost seemed as if they had calculated their chances of survival, deciding that a single butterfly being attacked would either be captured or not, and thus had a one-to-one chance for survival, while a butterfly flying in a group of twenty-four would have twenty-three chances of escaping if an enemy attacked, and only one chance of being caught. But since the Monarchs had not been endowed with a knowledge of the laws of probability, their behavior must have had some other source. Perhaps their compound insect eyes were beset by such a confusion of moving images that motion itself was too omnipresent to be considered a danger. Or perhaps it was yet another aspect of some universal mob psychology which compels the many to follow the few, regardless of what species of life is involved. Perhaps if thousands of individuals are gathered together, whether they be locusts or lemmings, shrimp or sheep, bats or buffaloes, Monarchs or minnows or men, they can be incited to mass action by the initiative of a few, so that when a few Monarchs abandoned caution, the rest followed suit. Perhaps in late afternoon when the population of the marsh began to melt away a few led many to places high in the tops of neighboring trees, while others settled on the shrubs of the marsh in the same way. This sudden indifference to danger must have been part of the whole incredible change in habits and behavior by which the Monarchs suddenly ceased to be free–roving, independent individuals and instead began gathering together in the security of immense congregations. Perhaps this revolutionary change was brought about by one last hormone which had lain dormant until finally some unknown stimulus had touched it and caused it to flow. . . .

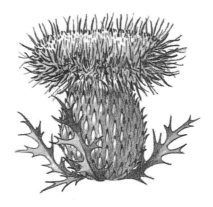

By the first of October there was hardly anything left blooming in the Meadow. There were a few pale heart-leaved asters, their disc-florets turned magenta with age, a few stalks of showy goldenrod, and one last superb thistle nearly three inches in diameter, the other blooms having already become prickly shaving brushes.

As he neared the fringes of the woods, the beams of Mr.

Stevens' headlights fell upon a young ash tree. Something in it moved quite suddenly and then grew still. He could not see what it was that had moved, nor where it was. Slowly and quietly he drew to a standstill and peered into the tree, waiting for his eyes to become accustomed to the lights and shadows playing among the slender yellowing leaves. Finally he was able to discover that the southeast side of the tree which faced him obliquely was bent down by a thick cluster — not a small cluster like the red berries which grew on some of the other branches, but some different thing, something much larger. He found the flashlight which he kept in his jeep and walked slowly toward the tree. In the beam of light which he cast upon it there was again that same sudden motion — an evanescent flash of golden-bronze: a warning flash that came and went in the fraction of a second, leaving nothing in its wake but the surprise of the beholder — and the congregation of Monarchs which had gathered there for the night became once more invisible. But this time Mr. Stevens had seen them open and close their wings, and he could make them out, hidden and small in the shadows. There were perhaps three or four hundred of them. It was a sight so unexpected and so unusual that he looked upon it with a kind of awe. The butterflies were just out of his reach, but he would not have touched them anyway. For the moment, the tree was theirs, not his, and he was filled with a sensation of very great pleasure. He did not know that scarcely one person in a thousand ever sees a little butterfly tree like the one in his meadow.

In Pacific Grove in California or in Lighthouse Point in Florida, it is possible to see the Monarchs at their over-wintering sites, where thousands of them remain from November to February. But here they roost so high in the trees that one can hardly see what they are. They could be the nest of some huge bird, or thick festoons of Spanish moss. No one would know that they are really butterflies, except that on warm days a few at a time come down to feed. But a little galaxy of monarchs resting for just one night is indeed a rarity. It seems a matter of pure chance that they should choose one tree and not another — one person's yard and not another's. They fly until near dusk, and then for the space of a single night one tree will be graced with their presence.

Very early in the morning when he went out to look at them once more, Mr. Stevens found that they had all disappeared as inexplicably as they had come.

XIV

Another End—
Another Beginning
(October 19–November 23)

Happiness is the shadow of things past,
Which fools still take for that which is to be!
And not all foolishly:
For all the past, read true, is prophecy,
And all the firsts are hauntings of some Last,
And all the springs are flash-lights of one Spring . . .

FRANCIS THOMPSON

BETWEEN SEPTEMBER sixth and October sixth there were in all about 12,000 Monarchs which passed through Eastern Point. But further south during this same time, 240,000 passed through a gap in the Appalachian Mountains. Flying by other routes from other places, there were countless thousands more, which were seen flying only briefly as they passed overhead, or which were seen feeding in small groups in inland marshes and meadows. Some were never seen at all, but would cross the plains numbering in the hundreds of thousands and pass the winter months in some hidden spot still kept a secret from all mankind.

But by the tenth of October there were only stragglers — the weakest, the smallest, the last of all the emergents, whose wings were perhaps not wholly sound. The marsh and all of New England was as if the Monarchs had never been there. The asters and the goldenrod had begun to tarnish. The royal procession — the shower of gold — was a thing of the past, and no more was left in its wake to mark its passing than is left by the memory of a dream.

The children of Danaus and his whole tribe flew along the beaches of New England and crossed small bodies of water with the wind. When they reached the Cape Cod Canal, they flew along its banks and continued south on the east shore of Buzzards Bay to Woods Hole. From there they crossed to Martha's Vineyard where they congregated at Gay Head. From Gay Head, they traveled over sixty miles across open water to Montauk Point, stopping only briefly to rest at Block Island. They congregated again at West Hampton, sixty miles further along the south shore of Long Island.

The following night they swarmed in trees at Long Beach, and early the next morning crossed the mouth of New York Harbor. Their group was not always the same, for some diverged to other routes, and found other Monarchs along the way, and it was never possible to know where the Monarchs along the endless stretches of sand and in the nearby countryside had begun their journey.

From a place near Red Bank on the south side of New York Harbor, they continued on down the coast to Cape May, New Jersey, where they waited three days for a favorable wind. Each day more Monarchs joined them, and by the time they reached Ocean City, Maryland, over 40,000 butterflies were swarming together in the trees. Here they encountered a heavy wind which forced some of them inland to Crisfield, and these followed the Del Mar Peninsula which forms the east side of Chesapeake Bay, while the rest followed the other shore of the same peninsula, so that all were again reunited at Virginia Beach.

Again at Virginia Beach strong winds assailed them, and many were swept inland across the Dismal Swamp as far as Winton, on the Chowan River which empties into Albemarle Sound in North Carolina. These flew down to Plymouth and across to Swanquarter, and other Monarchs joined them on the way. The remainder of the group flew to Kitty Hawk, and then they too reached Swanquarter. Here, for no apparent reason, they stopped. Each day for four days more butterflies arrived until at the end of the fourth day there were more than 100,000 Monarchs weighing down the branches of the trees.

On the morning of the fifth day, the sky was murky and long clouds distorted by wind were tumbling across the sky. After the clouds came a storm with gale winds and driving rains which lasted for a day and a night, but before dawn, of the second day the rain slackened as the clouds were blown out to sea. It was only after this, under a blue and docile sky, that the Monarchs took to the air once more in a long thin procession. Somehow they had been aware of the approaching storm and rather than risk being caught in the air in the midst of it, had waited for it to pass, protected by each other in the branches of the trees.

From Swanquarter to the Croatan National Forest, to the Orton Plantation and Carolina Beach, still in North Carolina, and still following the coast line, they came to Sullivans Island in South Carolina. South, south, ever south, until the huge mass of butterflies came to Sea Island, Georgia. It was the nineteenth of October.

About this same time, near Swan Island in the Caribbean Sea, there was a disturbance in the upper atmosphere — a little cold stream of air which began to mingle with the shimmering heat that had been rising from the surface of the water as the result of a week-long Indian summer.

As the swarm of Monarchs approached Sea Island, Georgia, there were more than 200,000 individuals following the same route. The first arrived on October nineteenth, and these pressed onward as more and more butterflies arrived, flying as high as 150 feet in the air in a steady stream which flowed without cease from seven o'clock in the morning to four in the afternoon for three days. The swarm separated at Sea Island, some continuing south in the direction of Lake Okeechobee, which is at the northern border of the Everglades. The others turned west toward Lighthouse Point, which is on the Gulf coast of Florida, south of Tallahassee.

But on the twenty-second of October, the migration came to a standstill. All that day and the next more Monarchs poured into Sea Island, but none departed.

Also, on the twenty-second, those which had pressed south toward Lake Okeechobee — perhaps 75,000 — came to a halt and huddled together in a huge drift on a live oak tree at Titusville Beach, about fifty miles south of Daytona.

The distance from Sea Island to Lighthouse Point could have been covered by the flock in four days with ease. From Titusville Beach to the Everglades was about the same distance, and yet these two agglomerations of butterflies would not move to complete the last lap of their long journey. The weather was warm and clear with light northerly winds. It seemed a perfect day for flying, but somehow the butterflies knew as they had known before. They knew what the weather bureau also knew, and what the people knew because they had been warned of it in the newspapers — that the little disturbance in the Caribbean Sea had begun slowly to gather — that winds and pressures and temperatures were giving it shape. It was performing a slow pirouette and at the same time starting to move in the direction of the channel which runs between the Yucatán Peninsula and Cuba, leading into the Gulf of Mexico.

The wind had begun like a sigh which no one had noticed, but gradually it rose to a groan — a whining groan still far away but so continuous a sound that finally it was heard, and it stirred uneasiness and dread in those who had heard it before. This was on the twenty-first day of October. During the night the wind gathered force, and on the morning of October twenty-second a gray pall hung over the horizon. The leaden surface of the gulf shivered and vacillated as though the timeless rhythms of its tides had lost their certainty. By noon the dread sound had risen to a roar as the storm wheeled into the Gulf of Mexico with the wind blowing at seventy miles an hour. At half past one it had blacked out the light of the sun, and flashes of blue and purple light coming from within the tortuous mass of cloud spread an eery incandescence across the darkness of the southern sky. . . .

All day long sea birds and shore birds could be seen spreading away from the storm's path, seeking in desperation some inland haven — some sheltered cove in which they might be saved from the devastating wrath of the wind. As the hurricane entered the Gulf it shifted its course, and late that afternoon its full force struck the west coast of Florida all the way from Sarasota to Inverness with a savage fury. The rain, which had fallen at first in stinging needles, now drove down upon land and sea alike in a black sheet. The waves were plowed into geysers — churned into columns of fluid stone which thundered against each other and the shore in a ceaseless, terrible cannonade. The wind at its peak knew no restraint but shrieked and screamed and tore at the land like a living creature bereft of all reason, yet possessed of strength beyond all reason. It bent the palm trees double beneath its lash, flung them to the ground, ripped out their fruit and sent it hurtling through the air to smash walls, windows, vehicles already crippled by the flooding streets. The few boats remaining in Tampa Bay were wrenched from their moorings and battered into splinters against half-submerged buildings and piers, or cast ashore where they were crushed together like walnuts. And above this screeching insanity, time after time came the sickening shudder of roofs being twisted and tortured and sent crashing against the nearest object left standing — of glass being violently broken — the terrifying sound of human voices trying to be heard as people trapped by the engulfing tides clung frantically to jagged pieces of floating wreckage which they shared with drowning animals.

The unfortunate birds which had been caught in the center of the storm were sucked into the air and imprisoned by walls of gyrating wind as the hurricane raged across the peninsula of Florida, leaving disaster and desolation in its wake. It wreaked destruction upon the land for fifteen hours before it reached the east coast and started out to sea once more, and by the time it reached the sea its viciousness had begun to slacken.

Sea Island, Georgia, seventy-five miles to the north, was out of reach of the claws of the hurricane and felt only the malevolence of its breath, which fanned the sea into cauldrons of foam and streamed through the trees so that they shook and jostled like mute bells. The Monarchs clung together in tight sheaves. The innermost were sheltered from harm by those on the outside, as leaves at the bottom of the heap are protected while those on the outside blow gradually away.

The southernmost edge of the hurricane struck Titusville Beach, and although its worst fury was spent, the winds were still so ferocious and the rain so cruel that the Monarchs, however dense and solid the cluster they had formed, however sturdy the tree in which they were huddled, could not prevail against it. Thousands were dashed to the ground and thousands more thrust into the sea to be regurgitated later on the beach in a long pathetic ribbon. The rest were propelled upward into the dizzying maelstrom as the hurricane surged out to sea. Some struggled to escape from the turbulence of the storm, and these were quickly torn apart. Some lowered their wings and drew their legs tightly against their bodies, and a few — a very few of these — were drawn into the eye of the hurricane and so might have been able to survive.

About 300 miles out at sea there was a tramp steamer sailing northeast from the Bahamas, bound for Bermuda and England and carrying a cargo of rum and cotton. The hurricane, gasping out its fierce life in fifty-mile-an-hour gusts, bore down upon it, whipping the sea into towering waves. All day long the ship lurched blindly on through the pelting rain, while a raw white chop spun across its decks and broke against its iron hull with a voice like crashing glass. Most of the live creatures which had been caught up by the onrushing storm had either escaped or lost their lives in an attempt to escape, but a few warblers, a small tern, and perhaps five or six hundred Monarch butterflies were still prisoners in the whirling mass. In the dark of night the dimming eye of the storm crossed the path of the freighter, and at dawn the wind — a wind of failing strength — blew against it from the opposite direction. Gradually the storm and its aftermath subsided. Somewhere in the broad expanse of the ocean it dissipated, and the sun rose one morning on a sea of glittering blue and great rolling billows upon which the freighter rose and fell, its deck strewn with butterflies. Many of them seemed to be dead, or nearly so, for they were unable to move. The astonished crew saved some for souvenirs, and swept the rest into the sea, but here and there on the ship a few — a very few — escaped unseen, and they clung precariously to whatever foothold they could find. Had the others really been dead, or, warmed by the noonday sun, would they have rallied and tried to find land once more? No one would ever know, for on shipboard there is no time and no room for such an observation.

The butterflies had descended upon the ship sometime during the early evening of the night before, but where they had come from was a mystery. Since Monarchs can fly only eighty miles in a day, and since they habitually roost for the night even before the sun has set, they could not have flown 300 miles over open water and arrived on the freighter's deck of their own volition. They must rather have been blown out over the sea by a strong prevailing wind. But where had the wind come from, and where had the swarm been captured by the wind? Had a westerly gale scooped them from a seaside meadow somewhere along the southern coast? Or had they been waiting and testing the wind on some desolate strip of land — some outer beach separated from the mainland . . . had they become disoriented when the wind blew from an unfamiliar quarter, and allowed themselves to be carried out across the ocean? Or was it possible that when the hurricane had died, the butterflies trapped within it — the last living Monarchs of the 75,000 or more which had been at Titusville — had somehow found strength to fly back toward land, even in the hours of semi-darkness, and in doing so come upon the ship once more? Such conjectures have no more logic in them than does the hurricane which alters its course, the tide which ebbs and flows twice in an afternoon, the tree which stands when all others are torn out by their roots, the swarm of lost butterflies which descends exhausted on the pinpoint refuge of a ship at sea. . . .*

Early the following month two Monarch butterflies were sighted in England, and a third battered specimen was caught by an amateur entomologist and sent to the British Museum, where it remains.

The Monarchs which rode out the storm at Sea Island, Georgia, were tattered and torn, but most of them survived. When the sun had finally dried them, they continued undaunted, and eventually completed the long, long voyage. Some crossed the Okefenokee Swamp and, traveling south-

---

* The above episode is based upon an incident which occurred aboard the U.S.S. *Joseph T. Dickman*, a Coast Guard vessel used for troop transport during World War II. The incident was reported to me by a friend who was a pharmacist's mate aboard the ship at the time.

The *Dickman* was en route from Boston to Capetown. During the war the exact routes of such vessels was not generally known, and the crew did not know the location of the ship at any given time. The U.S.S. *Dickman* was somewhere in a neutral zone following a generally southern course when butterflies descended upon it in such numbers that the decks were literally covered with them. The crew members who saw them alight reported a "swarm" of butterflies. Next day, the insects, although not dead, were too feeble to move, and had to be swept away when it became evident that those who had been crushed underfoot were causing the deck to become slippery. A shellback certificate shows that on this voyage the U.S.S. *Dickman* crossed the equator on November 24, 1941, at 40° 27′ W. Longitude. The invasion by butterflies had reportedly taken place before that time.

west, began to arrive in Lighthouse Point the first of
November. The others flew down the battered coast, and
in a week had found a roosting site in the Everglades.

Early in the afternoon of the day before Thanksgiving,
Mr. Stevens started out to spend one last weekend at his
cabin before closing it for the winter. It was a perfect
November day — cold enough to make his fingers tingle
and his breath whisk away in smoky puffs. The trees had
long since lost their leaves and stood along the edges of the
Meadow like gray skeletons — friendly skeletons standing
guard while the Meadow slept.

Mr. Stevens made a fire in his fireplace, lit his stove, and
started coffee before unpacking the jeep. There was much
to be done. The windows and doors must be boarded up,
and the larder made mouse-proof. The annual tree must
be felled across the path. Naturally last year's log could
not be used again because it served as roof for the foxes' den,
and the foxes must still be in it because just outside the
entrance there was a little pile of bones which looked like
the bones of a squirrel.

Then there was the last walk through the Meadow —
preferably early the next morning when there might be
frost underfoot. He liked to walk over the dried grass
after a frost when everything was covered with thin crystals of ice that crunched beneath his feet. It sounded like
something delicious being chewed — like very thin sugar
cookies with cinnamon on them. Then he would cook a
steak for his Thanksgiving dinner. By Sunday afternoon

everything would be in order, and last of all he would
padlock and bar the door. . . .

The next morning little crystals of hoarfrost had spread
in a thin crust over the meadow floor and the grass
crunched under his feet. He walked the boundaries of his
land, noticing all those things which were so well hidden
when the field was lush and green — the great holes of the
woodchucks, the grassy nest of the redwing, the piles of
rotting apples under the wild crabapple trees, and the gray
pouch which the oriole had woven without his ever having
noticed it was there. Ragna would like to have that for
her nest collection, he thought. What a child! She would
love the Meadow. Why had he never brought her here,
he wondered . . . He stood looking out over the part of the
world that no one but he himself enjoyed, and he thought
how different it would look if Ragna were out there plunging through the grass.

It came to him with a sudden shock that he had been
living in the past — that he had been trying to make the
Meadow into a mausoleum for his memories by keeping it
all to himself — by hiding in it. He had turned his back
on the present with all its bubbling laughter, and it had
been right there waiting for him all along — pulling him
by the hand! What a waste! But *next* year when vacation
came! *Next* year she would come! And it wasn't just
Ragna either. There must be dozens of children. He would
talk to the conservation people tomorrow. They might
want the Meadow, small as it was. And then all the children who wanted to would be able to come and explore.

Otherwise Ragna should have it, and perhaps someday her children would catch little green snakes here and see wings of flame rising to the sun.

At last everything was done. He took one last look around him and closed the door for the last time. As he drove away, he noticed that the Meadow was a soft universal brown — more tan than brown. The grass shone like the soft hair of little children, and the dried flowers, the ghosts of summer, stood stark and stiff — the goldenrod foaming with little silken tassels, the Queen Anne's lace lifting its brown chalices, the rest hardly more than stiff brown spears.

In the pods of the milkweed, the silk had lain in long damp threads, and the seeds had been packed tightly, one overlapping the other like scales. Then the pods had cracked, and in almost the same way that Danaus had emerged from his chrysalis and unfolded his wings to the world, the milkweed silk had dried and expanded and flown from the pods to scatter its seeds over the Meadow. Now the stalks were dry and leafless, with only the twisted remnants of their pods to show which flower they once had been.

List of Works Consulted

A Short Glossary

Map: Danaus' Travels

Map: The Great Southern
Migration

List of Works Consulted

Bates, H. W., *The Naturalist on the River Amazons*, reprint of 2nd ed. London: John Murray, 1864.

Berrill, N. J., "Living Clocks," *Atlantic Monthly*, Vol. 212 (Dec. 1963), p. 6.

Bonner, J. T., *The Evolution of Development*. Cambridge: Cambridge University, 1958.

Bouvier, E. L., *Psychic Life of Insects*. New York: Century, 1922.

Brown, F. A., Jr., "Living Clocks," *Science*, Vol. 130 (Dec. 4, 1959), pp. 1535–1544.

Brown, F. M., "New Bacteria Found in Insects," *American Museum Novitates*, No. 251 (Feb. 21, 1927).

Brower, J. V. Z., "Experimental Studies on Mimicry in Some North American Butterflies. Part I," *Evolution*, Vol. 12 (1958), pp. 32–47.

Buchbaum, Ralph, *Animals without Backbones*. Chicago: University of Chicago, 1948.

Clausen, Curtis P., *Entomophagus Insects*. New York and London: McGraw-Hill Book Co., 1940.

Comstock, J. H., *An Introduction to Entomology*. Vail-Ballou, 1964.

Coquillet, D. W., *Revision of the Tachinidae of America north of Mexico*. U.S. Dept. of Agric., Div. Entomology, Tech. Ser. No. 7, 1897.

Curran, C. H., *North American Diptera*. New York: Ballou Press, 1934.

Downey, John C., "Sound Production in pupae of Lycaenidae," *Journal Lepid. Soc.*, Vol. 20 (Aug. 1966), p. 3.

Ehrlich, Paul R., "The Integumental Anatomy of the Monarch Butterfly," *Science Bulletin*, University of Kansas, Vol. 38 (Mar. 20, 1958), p. 18.

———, "The Comparative Morphology, Phylology and Higher

Classification of Butterflies," *Science Bulletin,* University of Kansas, Vol. 39 (Nov. 18, 1958), p. 8.

Evans, Mary Alice, "Mimicry and the Darwinian Heritage," *Journal of the History of Ideas,* Vol. 26 (April-June 1965), p. 2.

Ford, E. B., *Butterflies,* New Naturalist series. London: Collins, 1945.

Holland, W. J., *The Butterfly Book.* New York: Doubleday, 1945.

———, *The Moth Book.* New York: Doubleday Page, 1914.

Howard, Leland O., *Insects,* Nature Library, Vol. 8. New York: Doubleday, 1904.

Klots, Alexander, *A Field Guide to the Butterflies.* Boston: Houghton Mifflin, 1951.

———, *Living Insects of the World.* New York: Doubleday, 1959.

———, *The World of Butterflies and Moths.* New York: McGraw-Hill, n.d.

Lanham, Url, *The Insects.* New York: Columbia University, 1964.

McDougal and Hegner, *Biology, The Science of Life.* New York: McGraw-Hill, 1943.

Mittwoch, Ursula, "Sex Differentiation in Cells," *Scientific American,* Vol. 209 (July 1963), p. 1.

Muller, Johannes, *Zur Vergleichenden Physiologie des Gesichtssinnes der menschen und der Tiere.* Leipzig: 1826.

Packard, Alpheus S., *Textbook of Entomology.* New York: McMillan, 1898.

Patton, Robert L., *Introductory Insect Physiology.* Philadelphia: W. B. Saunders, 1963.

Peterson, Bruce, "Monarch Butterflies are eaten by Birds," *Journal Lepid. Soc.,* Vol. 18 (May 1964), p. 3.

Remington, Jeanne E. and Charles L., "Mimicry, a Test of Evolutionary Theory," *Yale Scientific Magazine,* Vol. 32 (Oct. 1957), p. 1.

Scudder, Samuel, *Frail Children of the Air.* Boston: Houghton Mifflin, 1895.

Snodgrass, E. R., *Insects, Their Ways and Means of Living.* Smithsonian Series, 1949.

———, "From Egg to Insect," *Smithsonian Report* (1925), pp. 373–414.

Snodgrass, E. R., "Insect Metamorphosis," *Smithsonian Miscel.*, Vol. 122, Smithsonian Inst. Publication No. 4144 (April 1, 1954), p. 9.

Spector, William S. (Ed.), *Handbook of Biological Data.* Philadelphia: W. B. Saunders, 1956.

Tinbergen, Niko, *Curious Naturalists.* Country Life Ltd., 1958.

Urquhart, F. A., *The Monarch Butterfly.* Toronto: University of Toronto, 1960.

Wigglesworth, V. B., *Principles of Insect Physiology.* New York: E. P. Dutton, 1939.

————, "Metamorphosis and Differentiation," *Scientific American*, Vol. 20 (Feb. 1959), p. 2.

Williams, C. B., "The Migration of Butterflies," *Biological Monographs and Manuals*, No. 9, Edinburgh, 1930.

Williams, Carroll, "The Juvenile Hormone," *Scientific American*, Vol. 128 (Feb. 1958), p. 2.

————, "Metamorphosis of Insects," *Scientific American*, Vol. 182 (April 1950), p. 4.

Wolken, J. J., "Studies on Photoreceptor Structures," *Annals, New York Academy of Sciences*, No. 74, 1958.

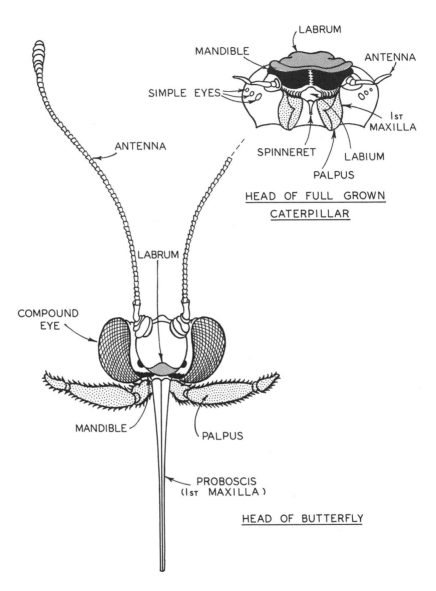

LABRUM

MANDIBLE

ANTENNA

SIMPLE EYES

1ST MAXILLA

SPINNERET

LABIUM

PALPUS

HEAD OF FULL GROWN
CATERPILLAR

ANTENNA

LABRUM

COMPOUND
EYE

MANDIBLE

PALPUS

PROBOSCIS
(1ST MAXILLA)

HEAD OF BUTTERFLY

Changes in structure of the head of Danaus plexippus
during metamorphosis

A Short Glossary
of Some Biological Terms

anal prolegs: fleshy appendages at the caudal end of the abdomen
of a caterpillar. Function as legs.

caudal end: the tail or anal end of the body of an animal.

chitin (chitinous): a chemical substance contained in the exoskeleton. It is associated with other materials which render
the skeleton hard, and is also found in the cremaster, the
lenses of the eyes and other hard insect organs.

chorion: the outer covering of an insect egg, which hardens into
a shell.

chrysalis, pupa: the inactive stage between the larva and the adult.
Pupa, from the Latin word meaning "girl" or "doll," is loosely
applied to this stage in all orders of insects having complete
metamorphosis. *Chrysalis*, from the Greek word meaning
"gold," is usually applied to the pupal stage of butterflies.

claspers: paired organs at the caudal end of the male butterfly used
for holding the female during mating.

cocoon: a covering of silk, often combined with other materials
such as leaves, bits of debris, etc., which surrounds and protects some moth pupae.

costal vein: the vein bordering the front edge of the wing of an
insect.

cremaster: a chitinous stalk at the caudal end of the chrysalids of
the families Danaidae and Nymphalidae and some other butterflies. Functions in holding the chrysalis in place during metamorphosis.

crystal cone: light-collecting unit of an insect eye. Located beneath the lens.

cubitus: the branching vein which borders the posterior part of
the discal cell in insect wings.

dorsal side: the back or upper surface, including the top of the
    wings.

ecdysis: the process of casting off the skin; a molt.

exoskeleton: the outer body wall of an insect, which serves to
    support and protect the inner organs.

hibernaculum: a protective covering for winter, or winter quarters
    of a hibernating animal.

instar: the stage between molts, so numbered that the first instar
    larval stage hatches from the egg and precedes the first molt.

larva (e): the immature stage of development which precedes the
    pupal stage; a caterpillar. *Caterpillar* applies mostly to moths
    and butterflies. *Larva* applies to the immature stages of any
    insect having complete metamorphosis.

maxillae: paired appendages on the head of an insect, modified to
    accommodate different food habits. Used by caterpillars for
    holding food.

metamorphosis: the series of changes of form during life. In
    butterflies from egg to larva to chrysalis to adult.

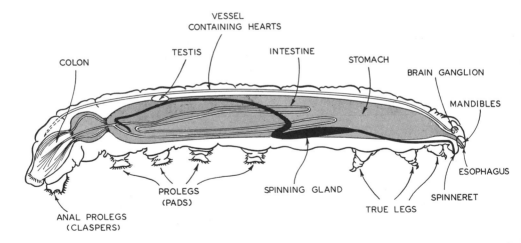

Comparison between the digestive system of the caterpillar of Danaus plexippus

omatidium: one complete unit of sight in the compound eye of an insect. (The simple eye of a caterpillar is an ocellus.)

ovariole: one of several minute tube-shaped organs in the reproductive system of a female butterfly, in which the eggs are formed.

oviduct: one of two branching tubes down which the eggs must pass in a female butterfly after leaving the ovarioles and before reaching the lower parts of the reproductive tract.

palpus (i): one of a pair of sense organs or feelers which are part of the mouth of an insect. The maxillary palpi are connected to the maxillae and located beneath the mandibles. The labial palpi are connected to the lower lip.

proboscis: a long coiled tube through which butterflies and some other insects obtain food.

protoplasm: the complicated self-perpetuating living material making up all organisms.

pupate: to change from larva to chrysalis or pupa. The change is made externally apparent by the shedding of the last larval skin.

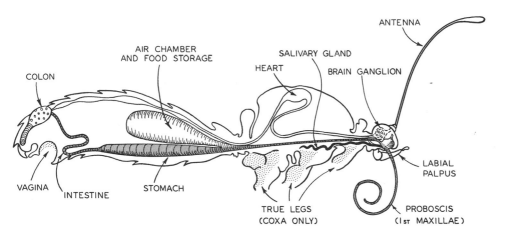

(♂ shown) and that of the butterfly (♀ shown)

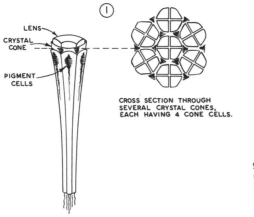

CROSS SECTION THROUGH
SEVERAL CRYSTAL CONES,
EACH HAVING 4 CONE CELLS.

CROSS SECTION OF ONE RETINULA

LIGHT ENTERS RHABDOME THROUGH
LENS AND CONE, IS TRANSFERRED
TO RETINULAE WHICH PERCEIVE
LIGHT.

ONE COMPLETE OMATIDIUM

SHOWING LENS SURROUNDED BY PIGMENT
CELLS, AND TOP OF CONE.

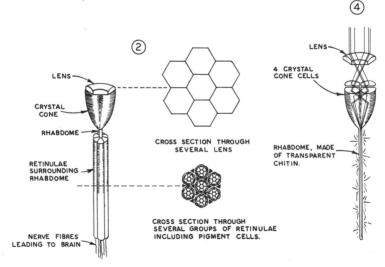

CROSS SECTION THROUGH
SEVERAL LENS

CROSS SECTION THROUGH
SEVERAL GROUPS OF RETINULAE
INCLUDING PIGMENT CELLS.

ONE OMATIDIUM WITH PIGMENT CELLS REMOVED

ONE CONE AND RHABDOME WITH LENS
AND RETINULAE REMOVED

Structure of the compound eye of a butterfly

retinula (e): light perceiving cells in an insect eye, which surround each rhabdom.

rhabdom: a crystaline rod which receives light and transfers it to the retinulae in an insect eye.

spiracle: one of several openings on the sides of the bodies of insects through which air enters into the tracheae.

tachina fly: any of a family of parasitic flies (Tachinidae) which are of inestimable value in the control of insect pests.

tarsus (i): the terminal segments or "foot" of the leg of an insect.

thorax: the center section of an insect's body located between the head and the abdomen, from which the legs and wings originate.

trachea (e): one of a system of branched tubules which conduct air from the outside to the tracheoles and thence directly to the tissues in the body of an insect.

tracheole: one of many tapering respiratory tubules in the tissues of insects, having blind terminal endings and originating from the ends of the smallest tracheae.

ventral side: the lower, or under surface of a body or part. The mouthparts, prolegs and legs of the larva originate on the ventral side.

vitelline membrane: membrane surrounding the yolk material in an insect egg.

walking proleg: one of several, usually eight, fleshy muscular pads provided with minute hooks. Located on the ventral side of caterpillars, they function in propulsion and as sense organs.

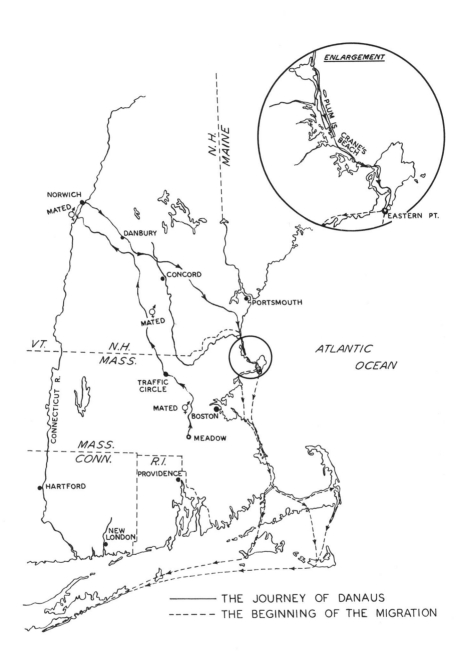

ENLARGEMENT

PLUM IS.

CRANE'S BEACH

EASTERN PT.

NORWICH
MATED

DANBURY

CONCORD

PORTSMOUTH

MATED

ATLANTIC
OCEAN

VT.   N.H.
        MASS.

CONNECTICUT R.

TRAFFIC
CIRCLE

MATED   BOSTON

MEADOW

MASS.
CONN.

R.I.

PROVIDENCE

HARTFORD

NEW
LONDON

————— THE JOURNEY OF DANAUS
- - - - THE BEGINNING OF THE MIGRATION

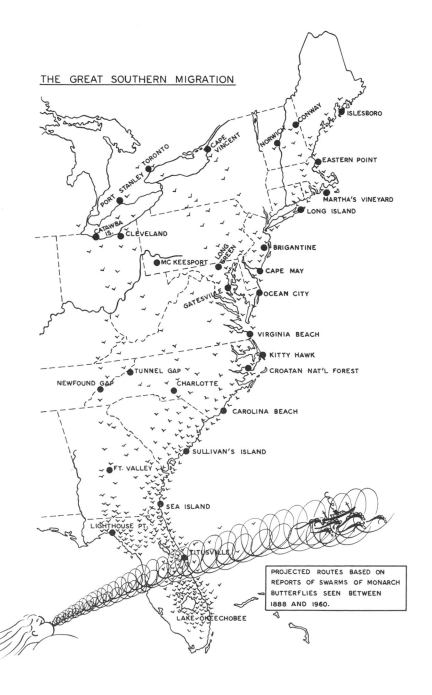

THE GREAT SOUTHERN MIGRATION

PORT STANLEY
TORONTO
CAPE VINCENT
NORWICH
CONWAY
ISLESBORO
EASTERN POINT
MARTHA'S VINEYARD
LONG ISLAND
CATAWBA IS.
CLEVELAND
BRIGANTINE
MC KEESPORT
LONG GREEN
CAPE MAY
OCEAN CITY
GATESVILLE
VIRGINIA BEACH
KITTY HAWK
CROATAN NAT'L FOREST
TUNNEL GAP
NEWFOUND GAP
CHARLOTTE
CAROLINA BEACH
SULLIVAN'S ISLAND
FT. VALLEY
SEA ISLAND
LIGHTHOUSE PT.
TITUSVILLE
LAKE OKEECHOBEE

PROJECTED ROUTES BASED ON
REPORTS OF SWARMS OF MONARCH
BUTTERFLIES SEEN BETWEEN
1888 AND 1960.